S260 Geology
Science: Level 2

C000184004

The Op

Block 2
Earth materials

Prepared for the Course Team by David Palmer and Glynda Easterbrook

The S260 Core Course Team

David Rothery *(Course Team Chairman and Author)*

Glynda Easterbrook *(Course Manager and Author)*

Iain Gilmour *(Multimedia Development Coordinator and Author)*

Angela Coe *(Block 4 Chair and Author)*

Other members of the Course Team

Gerry Bearman *(Editor)*

Roger Beck *(Reader)*

Andrew Bell *(Author)*

Steve Best *(Graphic Artist)*

Evelyn Brown *(Author)*

Sarah Crompton *(Designer)*

Janet Dryden *(Secretary)*

Neil Edwards *(Multimedia)*

Nigel Harris *(Author)*

David Jackson *(BBC)*

Jenny Nockles *(Design Assistant)*

Pam Owen *(Graphic Artist)*

David Palmer *(Author & Multimedia)*

Rita Quill *(Course Secretary)*

Jon Rosewell *(Multimedia)*

Dick Sharp *(Editor)*

Peter Skelton *(Author)*

Denise Swann *(Secretary)*

Tag Taylor *(Design Co-ordinator)*

Andy Tindle *(Multimedia)*

Fiona Thomson *(Multimedia)*

Mike Widdowson *(Author)*

Chris Wilson *(Author)*

This publication forms part of an Open University course S260 *Geology*. The complete list of texts which make up this course can be found at the back. Details of this and other Open University courses can be obtained from the Student Registration and Enquiry Service, The Open University, PO Box 197, Milton Keynes MK7 6BJ, United Kingdom: tel. +44 (0)845 300 60 90, email general-enquiries@open.ac.uk

Alternatively, you may visit the Open University website at http://www.open.ac.uk where you can learn more about the wide range of courses and packs offered at all levels by The Open University.

To purchase a selection of Open University course materials visit http://www.ouw.co.uk, or contact Open University Worldwide, Michael Young Building, Walton Hall, Milton Keynes MK7 6AA, United Kingdom for a brochure. tel. +44 (0)1908 858793; fax +44 (0)1908 858787; email ouw-customer-services@open.ac.uk

The Open University, Walton Hall, Milton Keynes, MK7 6AA

First published 1999. Reprinted with corrections 2002. Second edition 2007

Edited, designed and typeset by The Open University.

Printed in Europe by the Alden Group, Oxfordshire

ISBN 978 0 7492 1881 2

2.1

BLOCK 2 EARTH MATERIALS

CONTENTS

I INTRODUCTION TO BLOCK 2

I.I PLANETS, ROCKS, MINERALS AND ATOMS

Geology involves the study of our natural landscape, as a starting point for understanding how our planet changes through time (summarized in Hutton's maxim, 'the present is the key to the past'). In making the link between today's landscape and ancient or future landscapes, we need to understand the dynamic processes that sculpt the Earth – and to do this we need to understand the nature and properties of the geological materials from which our planet is made.

Most of the Earth is made of solid rock, and this is exposed at the surface and under the oceans. If you examine any rock closely, perhaps with a hand lens, you may see that what initially appeared uniform and bland is actually a rich mosaic of tiny particles, or **grains**. Rocks are no more than assemblages of finer-scale geological materials. They are the natural equivalents of concrete and ceramics. The basic units from which rocks are made are minerals.

Minerals are natural crystals, and so the geological world is largely a crystalline world. The properties of rocks, continents, and the entire planet, are ultimately determined by the properties of the constituent minerals, and many geological processes represent the culmination – on a very grand scale – of microscopic processes inside minerals. For example, large-scale processes, such as rock formation, deformation, weathering and metamorphic activity, are controlled by small-scale processes, such as movement of atoms (diffusion), shearing of crystal lattices (dislocation movement), growth of new crystals (nucleation, diffusion, crystallization), and phase transformations.

An understanding of mineral structures and properties also allows us to answer more immediate questions about the world around us, such as why quartz is so hard, and makes up the sand on our beaches; why window glass creeps and cracks with age; and why solid granite rock is destined to become soft, sticky clay. We must also not lose sight of the fact that minerals are natural resources, providing raw materials for many industries. Unlocking their secrets may have economic as well as geological applications.

I.2 INTRODUCTION TO MINERALS

Take a look at rock specimen (RS) 13 in your Home Kit. Note that this specimen is made out of a number of distinct types of grain: shiny black; cloudy white; and a translucent, grey variety. This is a collection of different *minerals*, which have grown together, to make an interlocking mass we call a **rock**. Minerals may also grow on their own – in cracks or cavities, precipitated from hot fluids. Such minerals tend to stand out because of their large size and well-developed crystal faces. Figure 1.1 shows one such gem-quality crystal of quartz (SiO_2).

Gem-quality crystals are objects of great beauty, and have been treasured for thousands of years. They have also been revered as objects of mystic power. Some of this reverence stems from a deep-seated fascination with their smooth crystal faces and geometric shapes. When so much of nature appears wild and irregular, what could have formed these geometrically precise objects?

(a)

(b)

Figure 1.1 A single crystal of quartz from Brazil; the specimen is 5 cm tall: (a) top view; (b) side view. (Crystal provided by Mike Henty)

We now know that the regular external appearance of crystals is caused by a regular internal structure: each crystal has a precise arrangement of atoms – its crystal structure – that leads to well-defined (and predictable) physical and chemical properties. Thus, a **mineral** is defined as:

> … a solid body, formed by natural processes, that has a regular arrangement of atoms which sets limits to its range of chemical composition and gives it a characteristic crystal shape.

Figure 1.2 shows part of the internal structure of quartz: you can see the regular arrangement of silicon and oxygen atoms, forming ring-shaped patterns of six silicon and six oxygen atoms (one such six-fold ring is indicated in the figure). The same, six-fold **symmetry** may be observed in well-formed single crystals of quartz, such as that shown in Figure 1.1.

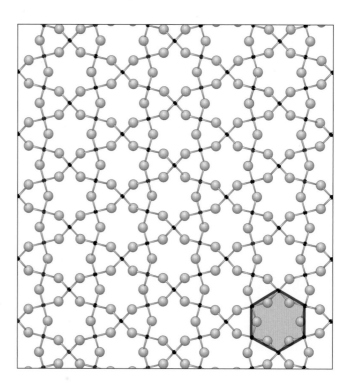

Figure 1.2 A part of the internal structure of the mineral quartz. It comprises an ordered array of two types of atom: silicon (shown here as small black spheres) and oxygen (large, light-coloured spheres). The 'sticks' represent chemical bonds between oxygen and silicon atoms. The distance between a silicon and an oxygen atom is approximately 0.16 nm (i.e., 1.6×10^{-10} m).

1.3 OBJECTIVES FOR SECTION 1

Now you have completed this Section, you should be able to:

1.1   Define what a mineral is.

1.2   Give examples of different kinds of Earth materials, and their length-scales.

Now try the following question to test your understanding of Section 1.

> **Question 1.1** (a) Use the quartz structure in Figure 1.2 as an example (atom centres at 0.16 nm intervals) to work out how many atoms laid side-by-side would be required to cover 1 mm.
>
> (b) Assuming the same packing in three dimensions, how many atoms are there in one cubic metre of quartz?

2 THE CRYSTALLINE STATE

2.1 STATES OF MATTER

As you may recall from previous courses, substances may exist in one of three different states: in a gas, liquid, or solid. Figure 2.1 illustrates these states in terms of their atomic arrangements. Atoms or molecules in a gas move at high velocities, and the distances between them are large (gases have low densities). In a liquid, the atomic motions are slower, and atoms are closer together (higher densities). If we were to take a snapshot of the atoms in a liquid or a gas, we would see a random (disordered) arrangement. Chances are, if we were to take another snapshot a fraction of a second later, it would look different. The internal structures of liquids and gases are said to be disordered – with respect to both space and time.

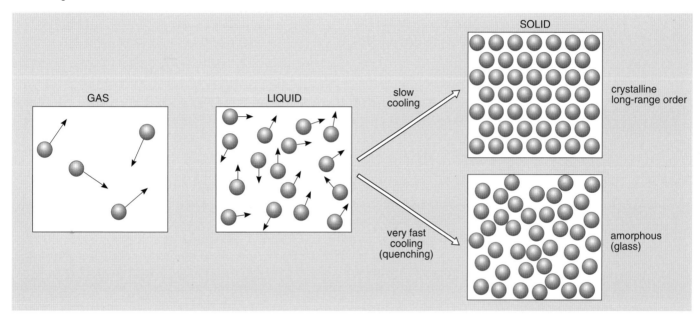

We can take a real-life snapshot of the liquid structure by very rapidly cooling, or quenching, the liquid so that it solidifies without time for the atoms to rearrange themselves. At low temperatures, there is not enough thermal energy for the atoms to move relative to each other. This means that the quenched material behaves as a solid: it does not appear to *flow* as most liquids do. This kind of disordered solid is called an amorphous (or glassy) solid. Window glass is an excellent example: this super-cooled liquid appears solid but, if left for many years, will show signs of flow (e.g., old window panes are sometimes thicker at the bottom than at the top).

Very slow cooling of a liquid allows atoms to arrange themselves into an ordered pattern, which may extend over a long range (millions of atoms). This kind of solid is called **crystalline**.

❑ The chemical composition of window glass is similar to that of quartz (a crystalline material): both are forms of SiO_2. Why is one material glassy, and the other crystalline?

■ Window glass is made by chilling molten SiO_2 relatively quickly; quartz crystals form when molten SiO_2 is cooled very slowly or by precipitation from solution.

We shall encounter examples of geologically formed glass later in this Block. It is important to note, however, that compared with crystalline solids, glass is not a

Figure 2.1   Schematic diagrams of the atomic arrangements in the gas, liquid and solid states. The arrows represent velocities of atoms or molecules in the liquid and gas. In a crystalline solid, atoms are confined to specific sites in a regular structure; in a glass, atoms are largely immobile, and the resulting arrangement resembles an instantaneous 'snapshot' of the high-temperature, liquid structure.

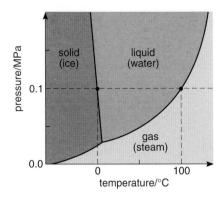

Figure 2.2   A phase diagram for the three phases of H_2O, showing the stability fields over a range of pressures, measured in Pa, and temperatures, measured in °C. (The SI unit of pressure is the pascal, abbreviated to Pa; $1 Pa = 1 N m^{-2}$; atmospheric pressure is approximately $10^5 Pa$, or 0.1 MPa.) The curves represent the boundaries between the different stability fields. Dashed lines are guide lines, to represent boiling and freezing at atmospheric pressure.

particularly stable form of matter. Over many years, glass may be slowly converted into a crystalline form in a process called devitrification. Sometimes you can see this in centuries-old window panes, where circular frosted patches of tiny crystals have formed within the glass.

We've mentioned that a single substance can exist as gas, liquid, or solid. We refer to these different states as **phases** of matter. A change of temperature may result in a **phase transformation**, e.g. from a liquid to a solid. For example, liquid H_2O (water) can be heated to form a gas (steam), or cooled to form a solid (ice). At particular temperatures and pressures, two phases may coexist (e.g., ice cubes floating in liquid water), but in general, only one phase will be found at a particular pressure and temperature.

We can represent the ranges of pressures and temperatures over which a particular phase is stable (i.e., its **stability field**), using a **phase diagram**, which is a plot of pressure against temperature bearing lines bounding the stability fields of each phase. Figure 2.2 shows an example for the three phases of H_2O. At the surface of the Earth, with a typical pressure of one atmosphere (approximately $10^5 Pa$), a crystalline solid, ice, is the stable phase of H_2O at temperatures up to 0 °C. Above this temperature (the melting point of ice), the liquid phase (water) is stable. The boundary between the solid and liquid stability fields is called a **phase boundary**, and is indicated by a solid line in Figure 2.2. If the temperature continues to increase at constant pressure (along the horizontal dashed line in Figure 2.2), the phase boundary between the liquid (water) stability field and the gas (steam) stability field is reached. This boundary represents the boiling temperature of water. Although we have only considered the effect of changing temperature, it is important to note that both the melting temperature and the boiling temperature vary with pressure.

❑   How would the boiling temperature of water, as measured at the top of a high mountain (where the atmospheric pressure is much lower), compare with its boiling temperature at sea-level?

■   Looking at the H_2O phase diagram, one can see that the boiling temperature of water (indicated by the liquid/gas phase boundary) decreases with decreasing pressure. Thus, on top of a mountain, where atmospheric pressure is lower, water boils at lower temperatures.

2.2 IDEAL CRYSTALS

Minerals are natural crystals: solid materials with regular, ordered arrangements of atoms. In this section we shall examine different ordered arrangements, their patterns and their symmetries. We shall also investigate why crystals have different shapes, and what this can tell us about their microscopic structures.

2.2.1 REPETITION THROUGH SPACE

From Section 1, you may recall that a typical crystal contains billions upon billions of atoms. It may therefore seem surprising that such vast structures can be described very simply. How is this possible?

A key concept is that of *repetition.* In the same way that some wallpaper or wrapping paper designs can be reduced to a basic unit that is 'tiled' in two dimensions, so a crystal structure (i.e., a three-dimensional arrangement of atoms in space) can be reduced to a basic, three-dimensional pattern (an atom, or group of atoms) that is tiled in three dimensions. Understanding this repetition is important: not only does it save us a lot of time when we need to describe the crystal structure, but it also gives rise to special crystal properties – one of which, diffraction of radiation, allows crystallographers to measure crystal structures in the first place!

Figure 2.3 illustrates the concept of repetition in two dimensions. Our repeating unit (referred to as the **motif**) is shown in Figure 2.3a. The motif is repeated at every one of a series of regularly arranged points, called lattice points. We can indicate lattice points more clearly by connecting them with grid lines, to form a two-dimensional net, called a **lattice**. Drawn in this way, the lattice contains a two-dimensional arrangement of **unit cells** (Figure 2.3b). If we now repeat the motif at every lattice point, we end up with the two-dimensional structure depicted in Figure 2.3c. Thus, a repeating pattern can be represented by two objects: a motif and a unit cell. This is an important principle, because it also applies to the structures of three-dimensional crystals.

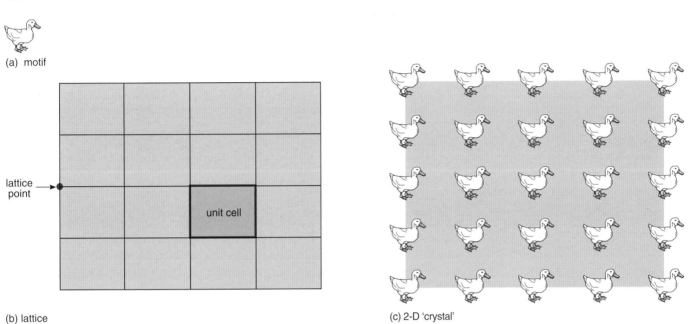

Figure 2.3   A simple two-dimensional pattern constructed by repeating a motif (a) at every point of a two-dimensional lattice (b). To describe the resulting two-dimensional pattern (c), all we need are the motif and the unit cell.

2.2.2 SYMMETRY

Many gem-quality crystals show evidence of symmetry at a hand-specimen level: they may have well-developed crystal faces, which appear to be related to each other precisely. Figure 1.1a showed a top view of a quartz crystal. The arrangement of some of the crystal faces gives this specimen a hexagonal (six-sided) outline. You could verify this by measuring angles with a protractor. For symmetry to exist at the visible, macroscopic level, there must be some microscopic origin, in terms of the arrangement of atoms in space.

❑   Figure 1.2 shows the arrangement of oxygen and silicon atoms in part of the quartz structure, viewed down the same direction as Figure 1.1. What evidence is there of hexagonal symmetry?

■   The structure contains large holes. If we start at the centre of one of these holes, and move outwards, we encounter a ring of six oxygen atoms; slightly farther out are six silicon atoms (black). If you draw lines between six neighbouring silicon atoms, you will get a perfect hexagon, as picked out in blue in Figure 1.2. (Note that the structure also contains smaller rings of three oxygen and three silicon atoms.)

Figures 1.1 and 1.2 show examples of six-fold symmetry. Other examples of symmetry are shown in Figure 2.4. Here we construct different patterns, by rotating an object (a duck) around an imaginary symmetry axis coming out of the paper. Each pattern is said to show rotational symmetry, relating one duck to another, in a slightly different orientation.

Figure 2.4 The effects of different **rotation axes** on a single object; the axes pass vertically out of the paper. A two-fold rotation axis (indicated by the solid ellipse) involves two 180° rotations; a three-fold axis involves three rotations of 120°, and so on. In general, an n-fold rotation axis involves rotational increments of $(360/n)°$. The position of each rotation axis is indicated by a solid shape: an ellipse, triangle, square, pentagon and hexagon for a two-, three-, four-, five- or six-fold rotation axis.

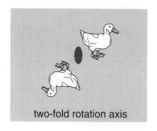
two-fold rotation axis

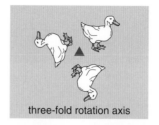
three-fold rotation axis

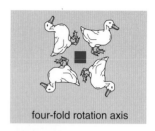
four-fold rotation axis

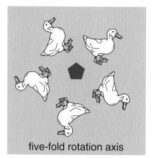
five-fold rotation axis

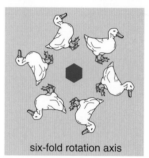
six-fold rotation axis

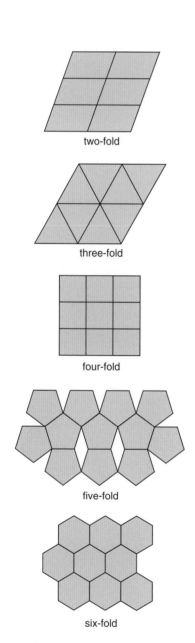
two-fold

three-fold

four-fold

five-fold

six-fold

Figure 2.5 Two-dimensional tiling. Some shapes cannot be tiled, without gaps appearing. Only two-, three-, four- and six-fold symmetry is consistent with periodic repetition.

2.2.3 REPETITION AND SYMMETRY

Each of the patterns in Figure 2.4 might be used as a motif, to build a two-dimensional structure. For this to work, the rotational symmetry of the motif must be compatible with the need to tile the motif throughout the lattice: some shapes, such as a pentagon (a five-sided object), cannot be arranged periodically – tiled – without gaps appearing. It is possible to show that only two-, three-, four- and six-fold rotation axes allow two-dimensional tiling (Figure 2.5), and hence these are the only kinds of rotational symmetry axis that we see in crystals.

In addition to rotation axes, we also find symmetry planes. The most obvious example of a symmetry plane is a **mirror plane** (Figure 2.6). Figure 2.7 shows a series of two-dimensional patterns, each with a different lattice and a different motif.

Activity 2.1

You should now do Activity 2.1, in which you will explore the concepts of repetition and rotational symmetry, by identifying unit cells, their motifs, and symmetry elements in a number of two-dimensional patterns.

2.2.4 THREE-DIMENSIONAL LATTICES

Real crystal lattices are three dimensional, and we could envisage building one simply by stacking a series of identical two-dimensional lattices on top of each other, as shown in Figure 2.8a. This process is a little like stacking sheets of graph paper. Now, in the same way that a two-dimensional lattice could be represented by the two-dimensional tiling of a unit cell, a three-dimensional lattice can be represented by a three-dimensional unit cell – which has a kind of box shape – repeated in three dimensions.

The characteristics of the two-dimensional lattices (square, rectangular, or oblique meshes) will clearly affect the three-dimensional lattice. Stacking square lattices could produce cube-shaped unit cells, stacking oblique lattices will produce sheared-looking shapes, and so on.

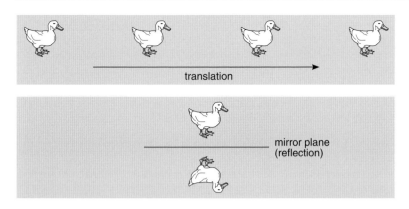

Figure 2.6 Repetition of an object in space (translation), compared with reflection (mirror plane symmetry).

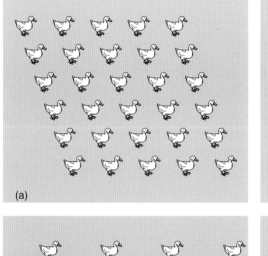

(a)

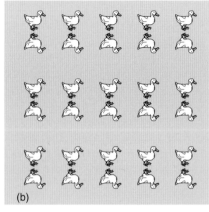

(b)

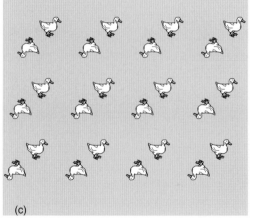

(c)

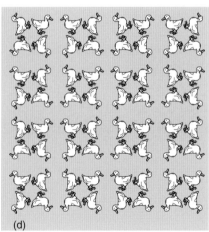

(d)

Figure 2.7 A series of two-dimensional patterns, each with a different lattice and a different motif. Some motifs have rotational symmetry and/or mirror planes.

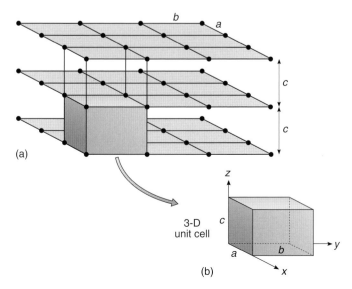

(a)

3-D unit cell

(b)

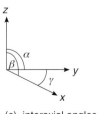

α = angle between y and z
β = angle between x and z
γ = angle between x and y

(c) interaxial angles

Figure 2.8 Anatomy of a three-dimensional lattice. (a) Stacking two-dimensional lattices results in a three-dimensional lattice. (b) A three-dimensional lattice can be represented by a three-dimensional unit cell. (c) Angles between the three crystallographic axes.

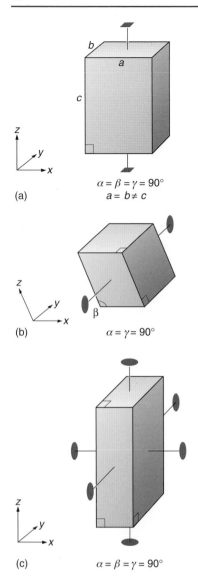

Figure 2.9 Symmetry and the shape of the unit cell. (a) A four-fold rotation axis requires that the crystallographic axes are at 90° to each other, and that the unit cell has a square cross-section. (b) A single two-fold rotation axis as shown constrains two of the crystallographic axes to be at 90° to each other. (c) Three two-fold rotation axes at 90° to one another imply that the three crystallographic axes are also at 90° to each other.

So that we don't get lost in the resulting three-dimensional lattice, it's convenient to specify some reference directions, x, y, and z, which are chosen to be parallel to three edges of the unit cell (Figure 2.8b). These are known as **crystallographic axes**, and it's important to realize that they are not always at 90° to each other! The angles between the axes are denoted by the Greek letters α, β, and γ (alpha, beta and gamma), as shown in Figure 2.8c. We can express the size of this unit cell by measuring the length of three edges, a, b, and c, as shown in Figure 2.8b.

This may seem a little involved, but we've managed to represent a three-dimensional lattice (which may have billions of lattice points) by just six numbers: the lattice parameters a, b, c, α, β, and γ. In the next Section, we'll see how the shape of the unit cell – and hence its lattice parameters – relate to a crystal's symmetry, and what effect this has on the external shapes of real crystals.

2.2.5 CRYSTAL SYSTEMS: SHAPE AND SYMMETRY

Just as some of our two-dimensional lattices showed symmetry, so three-dimensional lattices can also display symmetry. Of course, things are now more complex, because symmetry elements (e.g., rotation axes and mirror planes) could be in any direction. Some arrangements of symmetry elements place special constraints on the shape of the unit cell. For example, the existence of a four-fold rotation axis requires the unit cell to have a square section at right angles to the symmetry axis (Figure 2.9a). Three four-fold axes at right angles to each other imply that the unit cell must be cube-shaped, and so on.

We can classify crystals on the basis of this three-dimensional symmetry (and hence the shapes of their unit cells) into one of seven different **crystal systems** (Figure 2.10).

The beauty of crystallography is that we don't need to see the lattice, the unit cell, or the atoms, in order to deduce this microscopic-level symmetry. The external shape of a crystal (i.e., the arrangement of crystal faces) is controlled by its internal structure.

❏ Look again at the quartz crystal shown in Figure 1.1. What crystal system is implied by its shape?

■ The quartz crystal appears to have a hexagonal symmetry axis parallel to its length. The only crystal system that is compatible with this symmetry is the hexagonal system.

Generally, the more symmetry a crystal has, the more constraints this places on its external shape. Crystals belonging to the cubic system tend to have equidimensional shapes, such as cubes, octahedra, or rounded-looking crystals.

Some minerals, such as pyrite ('fool's gold', mineral specimen (MS) I in the Home Kit), have very simple cube-shaped crystals, which clearly indicate the underlying cubic symmetry. Other minerals have far more complex shapes, with many faces, and can look very daunting. However, if we focus on the symmetry relationships between faces, we might still be able to determine the internal symmetry.

It is important to realize that conditions during the growth of a crystal may prevent some crystal faces from growing properly, resulting in misshapen crystals. When we're looking at crystal symmetry, we must take into account the *angles* between faces, not the absolute sizes of individual faces.

Activity 2.2

In this Activity, you will examine a real crystal specimen, noting its shape and the arrangement of its crystal faces, in order to determine the overall crystal symmetry.

Crystal system	Unit cell	Essential symmetry	Everyday example	
triclinic	$a \neq b \neq c$ $\alpha \neq \beta \neq \gamma$	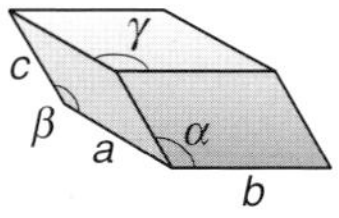 none	a packet of envelopes pushed askew in two directions	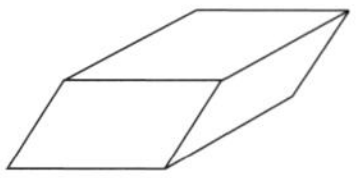
monoclinic	$a \neq b \neq c$ $\alpha = \gamma = 90° \neq \beta$	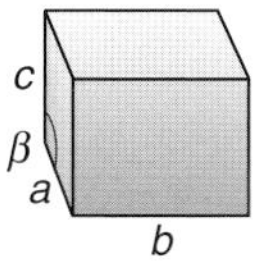 one two-fold axis	a partially squashed matchbox cover, flattened to one side	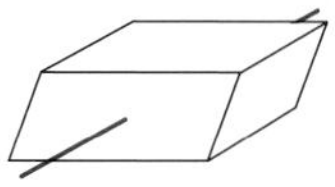
orthorhombic	$a \neq b \neq c$ $\alpha = \beta = \gamma = 90°$	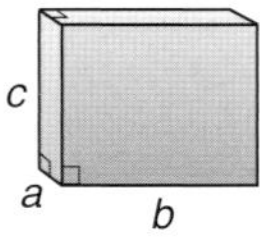 three orthogonal two-fold axes	a matchbox	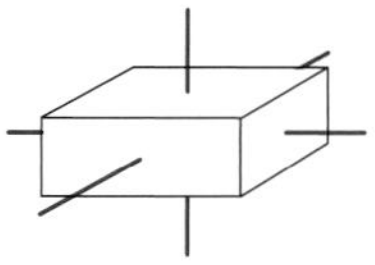
tetragonal	$a = b \neq c$ $\alpha = \beta = \gamma = 90°$	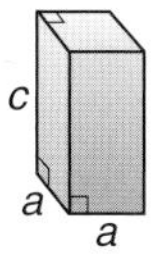 one four-fold	two sugar cubes stuck together	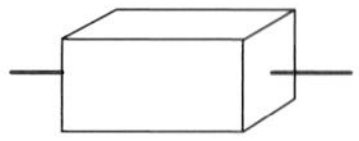
cubic	$a = b = c$ $\alpha = \beta = \gamma = 90°$	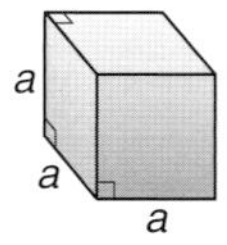 four three-fold axes (through corners)	a sugar cube	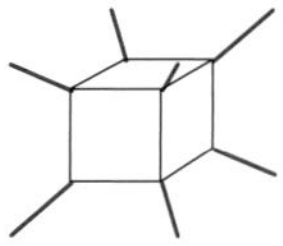
trigonal	$a = b = c$ $120° > \alpha = \beta = \gamma \neq 90°$	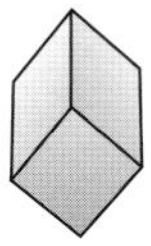 one three-fold axis	a 'Toblerone' packet	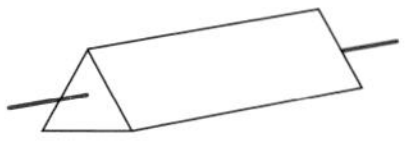
hexagonal	$a = b \neq c$ $\alpha = \beta = 90°$ $\gamma = 120°$	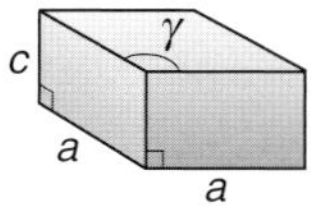 one six-fold axis	unsharpened pencil	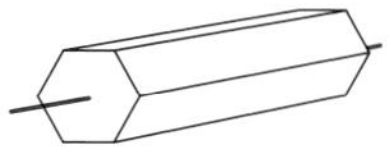

Figure 2.10   Illustration of the seven crystal systems, in relation to some everyday objects. Only the main axes of symmetry have been shown: there are many others, as well as numerous mirror planes.

2.3 INTRODUCTION TO REAL CRYSTALS

Having been introduced to the concepts of lattices, unit cells, motifs, and symmetry, you are now in a position to be able to study the structures of real materials. We shall begin by considering metals; pure metals may be quite rare in nature, but we can learn a lot from their crystal structures. For a start, they have some of the simplest atomic arrangements possible. In addition, we shall see that variations on these arrangements provide the structural foundations of many common minerals.

Activity 2.3

This Activity introduces you to some simple, three-dimensional crystal structures, using rotatable computer models. The concepts explored in this DVD are also described in the text, but because we are concerned with highly visual, three-dimensional patterns, you may prefer to complete this Activity *now*, before reading Sections 2.3.1–2.3.3. Otherwise, do this Activity at the end of Section 2.3.3 at the latest.

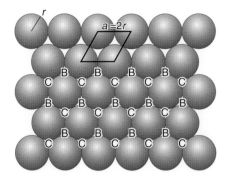

Figure 2.11 A single, close-packed plane of atoms. The unit cell for this arrangement has two sides of length $a = 2r$, where r is the atomic radius. An identical close-packed plane of atoms could be placed on top of this plane, with the upper atoms resting either all in the B sites, or all in the C sites.

2.3.1 CLOSE-PACKING OF SPHERES

Metal crystals are built from sheets of densely packed metal ions (ions are atoms that have lost or gained one or more electrons, leaving them positively or negatively charged). The ions are arranged in regular, **close-packed** arrangements (Figure 2.11), held together by free electrons (i.e., metallic bonding). This arrangement of ions in a close-packed sheet is like a raft of hard spheres (e.g., marbles) in contact with each other. (If you are unfamiliar with the different kinds of bonding that can exist between atoms, refer to Box 2.1 (p. 16), where these are summarized.)

The three-dimensional structure of a metal can be analysed in terms of the successive stacking of close-packed sheets on top of each other (just as we did in the previous Section, when constructing three-dimensional lattices). Let us start with a single sheet of close-packed spheres, as shown in Figure 2.11. We'll assume that all the atoms in this sheet are 'glued' together, so that the sheet behaves as a single, rigid unit. Now let's consider placing an identical sheet directly on top of the first one.

❏   What will happen to this second layer?

■   The second layer won't be very stable directly on top of the first one, and the whole layer will shift down and to the side slightly so that its spheres will come to rest snugly in gaps between the spheres in the first layer.

There are two sets of gaps formed in the first layer (Figure 2.11), labelled B and C. We'll assume that our second layer has fallen into a B orientation (and we'll refer to the orientation of atoms in the first sheet as an A orientation). Figure 2.12a shows the appearance of the two close-packed layers.

❏   What happens if we now decide to add a third sheet of spheres, directly onto the second layer?

■   As before, we might expect the new sheet to click into position, in gaps formed between spheres in the second (B) layer. But remember, we have a choice of two sets of gaps …

Looking at the B layer in Figure 2.12a, notice that one set of gaps lies directly over atoms in the bottom (A) layer. If we were to place our third sheet onto these gaps, both it and the bottom sheet would be in the same orientation (A). Moving up through the layers then, we would encounter an ABA stacking sequence.

Alternatively, the other set of gaps in the second layer has no atoms underneath it (these are the holes that are so clearly visible in Figure 2.12a). If we were to place our third sheet over the holes, it would be offset relative to both the A and the B orientations. We'll call this new orientation a C orientation. Moving up through the layers, we would encounter an ABC stacking sequence. Figure 2.13a shows the appearance of the three close-packed layers in an ABC stacking sequence.

We could continue to stack close-packed sheets on top of each other, remembering that each sheet can be in either of two orientations. However, most metals fall into one of two stacking sequences, either ABABAB… (referred to as **hexagonal close-packing**) or ABCABC … (referred to as **cubic close-packing**).

❏   Referring to Figure 2.12b, why is an ABAB stacking sequence referred to as 'hexagonal' close-packing?

■   The unit cell has its x and y axes at exactly 120°, and both are at 90° to the z axis (which is directly out of the paper). The edges of the unit cell parallel to the x and y axes (i.e., the a and b lattice parameters) are identical in length. Referring to Figure 2.10, you should see that this arrangement is indicative of the *hexagonal* crystal system.

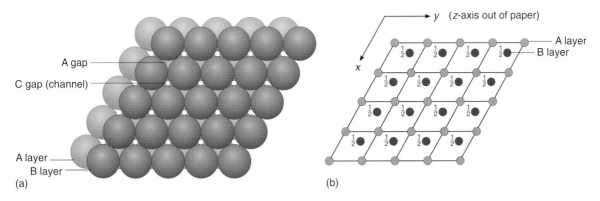

Figure 2.12 Hexagonal close-packing. (a) A three-dimensional model showing close-packed layers in an ABAB sequence along the *z* axis (direction out of the paper). (b) A two-dimensional projection of this arrangement, representing A-layer atoms by light blue circles, and B-layer atoms by dark blue circles. The B layer is displaced, in a horizontal plane, relative to the A layer. The $\frac{1}{2}$ placed next to each atom in the B layer reflects the fact that the B layer is halfway between two repeating A layers.

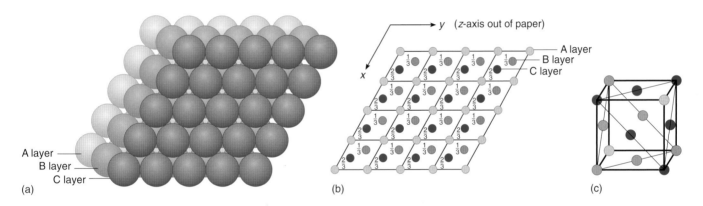

Figure 2.13 Cubic close-packing. (a) A three-dimensional model showing close-packed layers in an ABCABC sequence along the *z* axis (direction out of the paper). (b) A two-dimensional projection of this arrangement, representing A-layer atoms by light blue circles, B-layer atoms by mid blue circles, and C-layer atoms by dark blue circles. The $\frac{1}{3}$ and $\frac{2}{3}$ placed next to each atom in the B layer and C layer, respectively, reflects the fact that they are one-third and two-thirds of the way between two repeating A layers. (c) A cubic unit cell may be constructed from this arrangement.

❏ What is the motif for this lattice?

■ The motif consists of two atoms: an A atom (on a lattice point), and a B atom (offset horizontally and vertically relative to the A atom).

Cubic close-packing is illustrated in more detail in Figure 2.13b and c. There is a three-layer (ABC) repeat sequence, so the separation of two adjacent layers is one-third of the *z* axis repeat distance, as indicated in the projection shown in Figure 2.13b. Although we have drawn a hexagonal lattice in Figure 2.13b, this atomic arrangement can produce a cube-shaped unit cell, which is drawn in Figure 2.13c (the close-packed layers are inclined relative to the unit cell edges).

❏ What is the motif for this lattice?

■ The motif consists of three atoms: an A atom (on a lattice point), a B atom (offset horizontally and vertically relative to the A atom), and a C atom (offset horizontally and vertically relative to the B atom, by the same amount as the B atom is offset from the A atom).

Box 2.1 Bonding between atoms

Metallic bonding

Metallic bonding occurs when atoms donate one or more outer electrons to a free electron 'gas' (Figure 2.14a). This negatively charged electron gas flows between the (positively charged) ions, and acts as a kind of glue, holding them together. This kind of bonding is omnidirectional, so metal structures are dense and close-packed.

Ionic bonds

An ionic bond is formed by the *transfer* of one or more electrons from one atom to another atom, creating two ions of opposite charge, which are attracted to each other (Figure 2.14b; e.g., a positively charged sodium ion, Na^+, and a negatively charged chlorine ion, Cl^-). As with metallic bonding, ionic bonds can exist in any direction, so ionic crystals

tend to have fairly dense, close-packed structures. However, ionic bonds tend to be stronger than metallic bonding, so crystals containing many ionic bonds are much more brittle than metal crystals.

Covalent bonds

A covalent bond is formed when two atoms *share* two electrons, through overlap and merging of two electron orbitals, one from each atom (Figure 2.14c). Covalent bonding requires the precise overlap of electron orbitals, so if an atom forms several covalent bonds, these are usually restricted to specific directions. So, covalently bonded atoms in a crystal must be precisely positioned relative to one another, and the resulting structure tends to have a fairly low density (i.e., not as closely packed as metallic or ionic structures). (The precise positioning of H_2O molecules in ice results in a structure with lower density than that of liquid water, hence ice floats in water.)

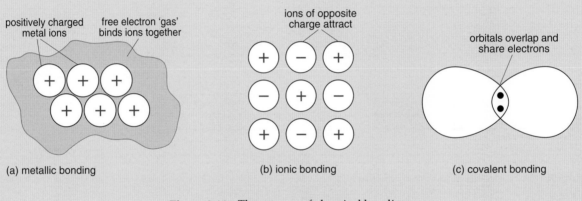

Figure 2.14   Three types of chemical bonding.

2.3.2 FILLING THE GAPS: IONIC STRUCTURES

Even though a close-packed structure like a metal looks densely packed, there are actually lots of spaces between the atom spheres. We call these spaces **interstices** and they are important because they provide sites for smaller, impurity atoms. The interstices also provide a basis for many **ionic structures**: they provide homes for smaller ions, in the presence of large ions. If we examine the structure of an interstice in some detail (Figure 2.15) we see that there are two kinds: tetrahedral interstices are surrounded by four atoms, at the corners of an imaginary tetrahedron; octahedral interstices are surrounded by six atoms, at the corners of an imaginary octahedron.

The mineral **halite** (rock salt) is an example of a structure based on the filling of octahedral interstices. Halite has the chemical composition NaCl. Chlorine ions are arranged a bit like the atoms in a metal – although they do not quite touch each other. The (much smaller) sodium ions fit snugly between the large chlorine ions, as illustrated in a space-filling model (Figure 2.16a).

The structure of the mineral **sphalerite**, which has the chemical composition ZnS, has a close-packed arrangement of sulfur ions, with the zinc ions filling half of the tetrahedral interstices (Figure 2.17).

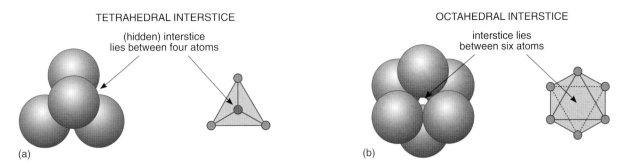

TETRAHEDRAL INTERSTICE

(hidden) interstice
lies between four atoms

OCTAHEDRAL INTERSTICE

interstice lies
between six atoms

(a)   (b)

Figure 2.15 Interstices (vacant sites) between two close-packed planes of spheres. (a) A tetrahedral interstice is formed between four close-packed atoms (three in the lower layer and one in the upper layer). The atoms are arranged at the corners of a tetrahedron (schematic figure on the right), with the interstice at its centre. (b) An octahedral interstice is formed between six close-packed atoms (three in each layer). The atoms are arranged at the corners of an octahedron (schematic figure), with the interstice at its centre.

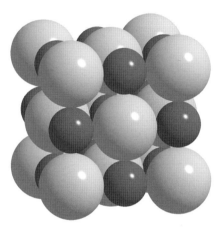

(a) space-filling model

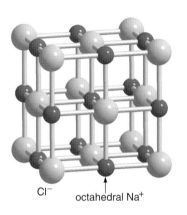

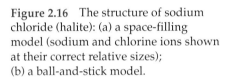

Cl^- octahedral Na^+

(b) ball-and-stick model

Figure 2.16 The structure of sodium chloride (halite): (a) a space-filling model (sodium and chlorine ions shown at their correct relative sizes); (b) a ball-and-stick model.

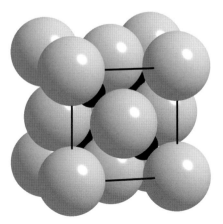

(a) space-filling model

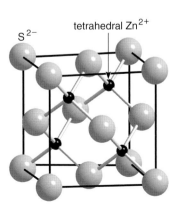

S^{2-} tetrahedral Zn^{2+}

(b) ball-and-stick model

Figure 2.17 The structure of zinc sulfide (sphalerite): (a) a space-filling model. (b) a ball-and-stick model. The unit cell is picked out with black lines.

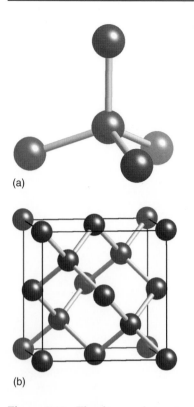

(a)

(b)

Figure 2.18 The diamond structure: (a) the tetrahedral arrangement of covalent bonds around a carbon atom; (b) the arrangement of atoms and bonds in a unit cell: the unit cell is outlined in black.

2.3.3 COVALENT STRUCTURES

Halite and sphalerite have ionic bonds, and relatively simple structures. Crystals containing *covalent* bonds tend to have more complex structures. Unlike metallic or ionic bonds, covalent bonds are directional, and this places additional constraints on the arrangements of atoms within such a crystal. One result is that **covalent structures** tend to be more open – and hence have lower densities – than metallic or ionic structures.

One example of a covalently bonded solid is the mineral **diamond**. Diamond is a form of carbon, in which each atom is covalently bonded to four other carbon atoms, arranged at the corners of a tetrahedron (Figure 2.18a). The resulting structure, which has a cubic unit cell, is illustrated in Figure 2.18b.

Contrast this structure – and its large unit cell – with the hexagonal close-packed metal structure depicted in Figure 2.12. Both structures involve just one kind of atom, but the covalent (diamond) structure is far more complex, and contains much more free space, than the metallic structure.

Another form of carbon is **graphite**. Compared with diamond, the carbon atoms in graphite have a slightly different kind of bonding. Each carbon is covalently bonded to *three* neighbours in the same plane (Figure 2.19a), and the result is a strong sheet of carbon atoms. Each carbon atom has one extra electron available for bonding. These form very weak bonds at right angles to the plane, which serve to keep the carbon sheets together (Figure 2.19b).

❑ How do the crystal structures of diamond and graphite explain the different hardnesses of the two minerals?

■ Diamond has a three-dimensional bonding pattern, with identical bonding in all directions, and no 'weak' directions. Diamond is therefore expected to be a very hard material. In contrast, graphite has a predominantly two-dimensional bonding pattern, consisting of sheets of C–C bonds. The bonds between the sheets are very weak, so it should be relatively easy for adjacent sheets to slide past each other. Graphite is therefore expected to be a very soft material (and indeed it is, which is why it is used as a dry lubricant).

Diamond and graphite have the same chemical composition (pure carbon) but different crystal structures. They are known as **polymorphs** of carbon. Diamond is formed under different conditions (high pressures and temperatures) from graphite (low pressures and temperatures), and is less stable than graphite at the surface of the Earth. However, because of the strong bonding in diamond, it is very difficult to break down the diamond structure, so diamonds will not spontaneously convert into graphite!

If you have not done Activity 2.3 yet, we recommend that you do it now, to reinforce your understanding of Section 2.3.

Figure 2.19 The graphite structure: (a) the triangular arrangement of covalent bonds around a carbon atom; (b) part of the three-dimensional structure of graphite, showing strongly bonded hexagonal sheets of carbon atoms, connected by weak bonds.

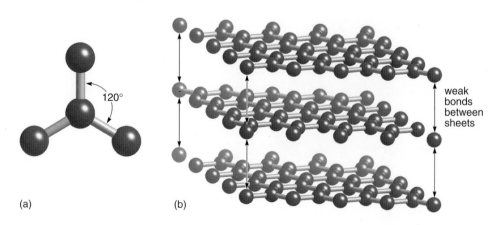

120°

(a)   (b)

weak bonds between sheets

2.4 DEFECTS IN CRYSTALS

Virtually all crystals contain minute imperfections, or defects. These may be as simple as a missing atom, or extra planes of atoms inserted into the structure. The effect of defects on the physical and chemical properties of a crystal is out of all proportion to their concentration! The rate of diffusion of atoms through a crystal lattice – which determines how processes such as weathering, or other chemical reactions will proceed – is critically related to the presence of defects, as is the mechanical strength of a crystal (which determines the strength of rocks, and how they are likely to deform under intense pressure). Individual defects may seem minute, but their geological importance cannot be overemphasized.

2.4.1 POINT DEFECTS

Point defects may involve missing or displaced atoms in a crystal structure, giving rise to empty sites, or vacancies. Such defects are referred to as intrinsic defects. Defects often occur in pairs: for example, a missing positively charged ion is compensated by a missing negatively charged ion, so that the crystal has no net electrical charge. The presence of intrinsic defects makes it much easier for atoms to diffuse through the crystal structure, by moving between vacant sites (Figure 2.20a).

Minerals are never chemically pure, and always contain some foreign atoms. These can be considered as extrinsic defects ('from outside the crystal'). Where are these impurity atoms found? One possibility is that they squeeze into interstices (Figure 2.20b). Another possibility is that they may directly replace (substitute for) atoms in the ideal structure – although, for a comfortable fit, the substituting atom must have a similar size, and charge, to the original atom. One common substitution is Fe^{2+} for Mg^{2+}, as occurs in the mineral olivine.

Sometimes we can see the effect of defects just by looking at a mineral: point defects can cause otherwise uncoloured minerals to become coloured. Minerals appear coloured when light is absorbed as it passes through the crystal structure. The mechanism for the absorption of light involves excitation of weakly bonded electrons, which tend to be found close to vacancies (e.g., a vacancy created by removing a negatively charged ion will have a net positive charge, and this attracts (loosens) electrons from nearby atoms or ions). This kind of colour-inducing point defect is called a colour centre, and can also be induced by subjecting a crystal to radioactivity (some jewellers deliberately irradiate their gemstones in order to create, or enhance, vivid colours!).

2.4.2 LINE DEFECTS

Minerals taken from deformed rocks are found to contain large numbers of line defects. Figure 2.21 shows an artificial example. Line defects are caused by rows of atoms that are out of place in a crystal lattice. The most common type of line defect is caused by an extra half-plane of atoms inserted into the crystal structure – a bit like a bookmark placed inside a book. The *line* of atoms at the edge of this extra plane have 'dangling bonds' and appear dislocated from the rest of the crystal. This line of atoms is referred to as an edge dislocation (Figure 2.22). We shall see that dislocations are the key to understanding how minerals – and hence rocks – deform.

What happens when a crystal is made to deform? One might think of the planes of atoms in a crystal as being like cards in a pack of playing cards; deforming the crystal could result in the planes sliding over each other – just as playing cards do when the pack is sheared. Unfortunately, this simple analogy

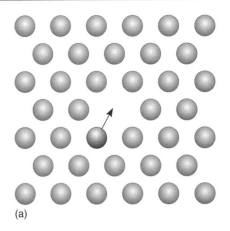
(a)

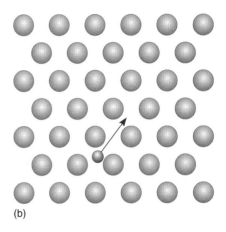
(b)

Figure 2.20 Point defects and diffusion mechanisms: (a) a point defect caused by a vacancy helps atoms to diffuse; (b) an extrinsic defect consists of an impurity atom in an interstitial site, and diffusion occurs along a pathway between sites.

Figure 2.21 Transmission electron microscope image showing many line defects in a crystal of indium aluminium arsenide. Each dark line represents a strained part of the crystal. The width of this image is about 1 μm.

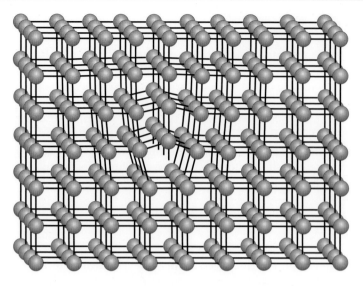

Figure 2.22   A three-dimensional diagram showing an edge dislocation – an extra half-plane of atoms in the crystal.

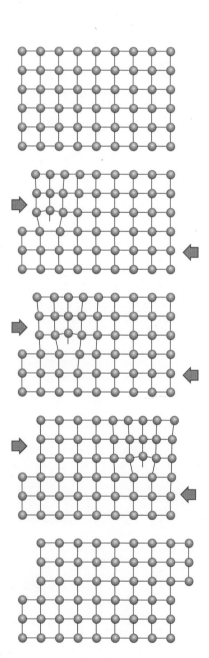

Figure 2.23   The movement of a dislocation through a crystal under stress forces, represented by the arrows. The two-dimensional plans represent successive stages in the deformation of the crystal lattice.

turns out to be inappropriate for crystals, which have very strong bonds between the planes: to slide two planes against each other would require all of the bonds between the planes to be broken in one step, and this would require phenomenal amounts of energy, and probably destroy the crystal!

It turns out that crystals deform in a number of small steps. At each step, only the set of bonds along a dislocation line are broken (and at the same time, the previously broken bonds are re-formed). The process works a bit like a zip that is fastened at both ends. Only the region around the dislocation (the zipper) is ever unzipped. As the dislocation moves forward, it 'unzips' a new region of crystal, whilst simultaneously zipping-up the region behind. This step-by-step process requires much less energy than breaking all of the bonds between two planes in one big wrench. Under stress, the dislocation line passes through the crystal, moving perpendicular to its length, and eventually creating a small step at either end of the crystal. This process is illustrated in Figure 2.23.

The strength of a crystal depends on the amount of force required to move the dislocation through the crystal, which relates to the strength of chemical bonds, and the size of the step created. Crystals with weak, metallic bonds are much easier to deform than crystals with strong, covalent bonds (such as diamond). Close-packed structures such as metals also have very small dislocation steps (of the order of 0.1 nm) and are much easier to deform (they are more malleable) than many mineral structures, which have larger steps (of the order of 1–2 nm), and consequently tend to be brittle rather than malleable. Incidentally, metals can be strengthened by introducing impurity atoms – either as extrinsic point defects, or as tiny crystals (precipitates) of other phases – which impede the progress of dislocations through the structure. Thus, steel (containing iron–carbon alloy precipitates) is a stronger engineering material than pure iron.

2.4.3   Planar defects

Crystals grow by the progressive addition of atoms onto a surface – a process called nucleation. 'Mistakes' in the stacking of new planes with respect to previously formed planes are very common during crystal growth.

In Section 2.3.1, you saw how identical layers of close-packed atoms could be stacked in precise sequences, to build three-dimensional structures. Each close-packed layer has two sets of holes, on which another layer can be placed, and this gave the option of different stacking sequences (e.g., ABABAB ... hexagonal close-packing, and ABCABC ... cubic close-packing). However, because each layer could be added in one of two positions, there is always the possibility of getting out-of-sequence stacking. For example, instead of an ordered ABCABC sequence, we might get ABC**B**CABC ... The errant **B** layer is called a stacking fault, and this sequence is illustrated in Figure 2.24a.

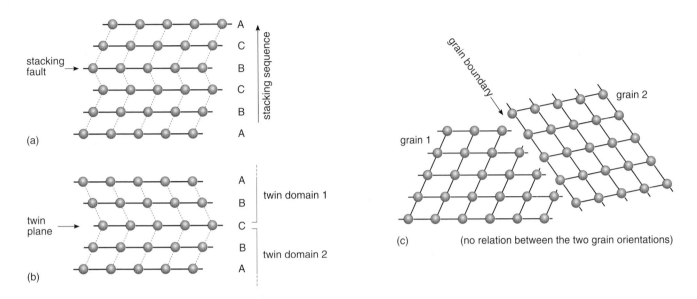

Figure 2.24 Different kinds of planar defect. (a) Stacking of close-packed planes (here seen side-on) can sometimes result in stacking faults. (b) A twin boundary separates two regions of a crystal that are mirror images. The two regions are referred to as twin domains. (c) Grain boundaries are different from twin boundaries because there is no orientation relationship between crystals on either side of the boundary, i.e., there are two distinct grains.

Continuing with our close-packing models, it is also possible to develop a kind of stacking fault that divides a crystal into two regions that are exact mirror images of each other. In our previous example, the stacking fault was limited to one plane out of sequence, and the normal stacking sequence resumed. Another possibility is the sequence ABCAB**C**BACBA. The stacking fault at the **C** plane results in two mirror images of crystal, both in ABCABC stacking sequences (try reading the sequence from right to left). This crystal is said to be **twinned**, with a central C layer acting as the boundary, or twin plane, between two twin components (Figure 2.24b).

So far we have considered planar boundaries between different regions within the same crystal. If two crystals are joined together, their boundary is called a **grain boundary** (Figure 2.24c). Grain boundaries are found in many metals, and in rocks where crystals have grown adjacent to each other during crystallization from a melt (e.g., quartz and feldspar crystals in granite), or have been forced against each other at very high pressures (e.g., calcite crystals in marble).

2.5 PHYSICAL PROPERTIES OF MINERALS: THE HAND-SPECIMEN LEVEL

We have seen how some physical properties of crystals, such as hardness and crystal shape, can be related to specific crystal structures. We also saw that other properties, such as mechanical strength and colour, are affected by defects in crystal structures. The important point to note is that because minerals have well-defined crystal structures, they also have predictable physical properties.

In this Section, we shall review some of the physical properties of minerals that can be observed, and tested, at a hand-specimen level. We can use these properties as a basis for recognizing and distinguishing different minerals, in the knowledge that differences at the hand-specimen level reflect fundamental differences at the microscopic level.

2.5.1 DENSITY

The density of a mineral depends on the chemical composition of the mineral and, as we've seen earlier, the type of bonding and the crystal structure. Some of the least dense minerals have very open crystal structures, with covalent bonds. The densest minerals have tightly packed crystal structures, often with metallic bonding. Table 2.1 lists the relative densities for some minerals, compared with that for water at ambient temperatures (the absolute density of water at ambient temperature is approximately $1000 \, \text{kg m}^{-3}$).

Table 2.1 Relative densities of some minerals and other solids.

Substance	Relative density at room conditions (compared with water)	Structure and bonding
ice, H_2O	0.9	open structure; covalent bonds plus weak bonds between H_2O molecules
graphite, C	2.2	open structure; covalent bonds plus weak bonds between layers
feldspar, $KAlSi_3O_8$	2.5	open structure; predominantly covalent bonds
quartz, SiO_2	2.7	open structure; predominantly covalent bonds
olivine, $Mg_2SiO_4 - Fe_2SiO_4$	3.2–4.4	structure based on close-packing, but with ionic and covalent bonds. Density increases as Fe content increases
diamond, C	3.5	structure based on close-packing, but with covalent bonds
barite, $BaSO_4$	4.5	ionic bonds between barium and sulfate groups
haematite (iron oxide), Fe_2O_3	5.3	structure based on close-packing; ionic and metallic bonds
galena (lead sulfide), PbS	7.6	structure based on close-packing; ionic and metallic bonds
silver, Ag	10.5	close-packed structure; metallic bonds
gold, Au	19.3	close-packed structure; metallic bonds

You can get a general idea of the relative densities of different minerals just by lifting a mineral fragment: a piece of metallic lead (Pb) feels heavier than a piece of window glass (amorphous SiO_2) of the same size.

2.5.2 COLOUR

The colour of a mineral can be its most memorable feature, but colour is possibly one of the least reliable properties for identifying minerals. Many minerals can show a wide range of coloration. You've already seen that the presence of point defects in a crystal lattice can give rise to colour – even in minerals that are not usually coloured. For example, quartz is colourless when pure, but can develop striking colours (purple, orange, pink, black) when irradiated (to produce point defects) or when its lattice contains small amounts of other elements, such as iron or titanium. (Some coloured varieties of quartz are illustrated in Plate 4.1.)

Some minerals do have reliable and distinctive colours, however. Minerals that contain large amounts of iron and/or magnesium are typically dark green or black. These include the minerals olivine and pyroxene, which are examples of the so-called **mafic minerals** (sometimes referred to as **ferromagnesian minerals**).

2.5.3 CRYSTAL SHAPE

Single crystals of minerals may develop beautiful shapes, with smooth, well-developed faces. You've seen that the shape of a crystal relates to its internal structure, and that the symmetry of a single crystal is the outward expression of the microscopic symmetry of the atomic arrangements inside the crystal lattice.

There are many terms used to describe the shapes of different crystals, but we can broadly group mineral shapes into one of three categories (Figure 2.25): prismatic (the crystal is stretched out along one direction), tabular (the crystal is squashed along one direction, so appears plate-like), or equidimensional (the crystal has similar appearance in different directions, e.g., cubes, octahedra, or 'rounded' crystals).

It is important to realize that the exact shape of a crystal can vary, because of different conditions at the time of growth. You will often find two crystals of the same mineral that differ in the relative sizes of specified crystal faces – and faces that are present in one specimen may not be visible in another. Although the *sizes* of specific crystal faces frequently vary, the *angles* between such faces are always fixed: they are defined by the crystal structure.

2.5.4 LUSTRE

The term **lustre** refers to the surface appearance of a mineral. Typical terms used to describe a mineral's lustre include glassy (or vitreous), greasy, waxy, and metallic. The lustre of a mineral depends on the way in which its surfaces reflect light. Minerals with metallic bonding scatter light very strongly, giving rise to shiny, reflective surface appearances and metallic lustre. Other types of bonding can give different kinds of lustre, depending on the chemical composition, the bonding, and the structure at a mineral surface.

2.5.5 CLEAVAGE

If a crystal is struck with a hammer, it will probably shatter into many tiny pieces. Some minerals, such as quartz, break into irregular, glassy fragments. Other minerals, such as calcite, break into well-defined blocky shapes, called cleavage fragments; they are said to have the property of **cleavage**. Cleavage arises when the crystal structure of a mineral contains weak directions, or

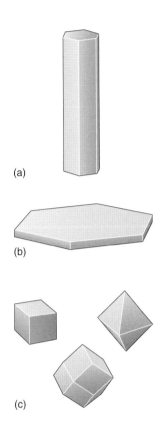

(a)

(b)

(c)

Figure 2.25 Some examples of crystal shapes: (a) prismatic (quartz – grows in the hexagonal system); (b) tabular (mica – also grows in the hexagonal system); (c) equidimensional (pyrite – grows in the cubic system).

planes; when subjected to stress (e.g., a hammer blow), the crystal will preferentially break cleanly along the weak directions. Later in this Block we shall examine the mineral mica, which has such perfect cleavage that you can readily split, or cleave, wafer-thin sheets from a crystal, using just a fingernail.

2.5.6 HARDNESS

Hardness is loosely defined as the resistance of a material to scratching, or indentation. Hardness is affected by weaknesses in the crystal structure, which may occur in particular directions (e.g., diamond is harder than graphite). The absolute hardness of a material can be measured very precisely, using a machine to determine the indentation of a special probe into a crystal surface. However, we can get a general idea of a mineral's *relative* hardness, by undertaking a few simple scratch tests.

The 19th century German mineralogist, Friedrich Mohs, devised a scale of mineral hardnesses, consisting of carefully chosen common minerals, ranked in order of increasing hardness, from talc, with a hardness of 1, to diamond, with a hardness of 10. Compared with an absolute hardness scale, **Mohs' scale** is decidedly non-linear (diamond is actually several times harder than corundum!), but because it uses common minerals, it provides a quick and easy reference for the geologist in the field (Table 2.2). Minerals with a hardness of less than 2.5 may be scratched by a fingernail; those with a hardness of less than 3.5 may be scratched by a copper coin, etc. Likewise, a mineral of hardness 7 will scratch a mineral of hardness 6.

Table 2.2 Mohs' hardness scale.

Mohs' hardness	Reference mineral	Non-mineral example
1	talc	
2	gypsum	
(2.5)	⟵—————	fingernail
3	calcite	
(3.5)	⟵—————	copper coin
4	fluorite	
5	apatite	
(5.5)	⟵—————	window glass/penknife blade
6	feldspar	
(6.5)	⟵—————	hardened steel file
7	quartz	
8	topaz	
9	corundum	
10	diamond	

Hardness should not be confused with toughness, which is the resistance of a material to breaking. Many minerals are hard, but not tough – for instance, diamond is the hardest-known material, but is not tough: it will shatter if dropped onto a hard surface. In contrast, the material known as jade (actually a composite of two minerals, jadeite and nephrite) is extremely tough, but not hard as it is quite easy to scratch jade jewellery.

Activity 2.5

You should now do Activity 2.5 using 'Properties of minerals' on DVD 1 (Block 2 Earth Materials).

2.6 OBJECTIVES FOR SECTION 2

Now you have completed this Section, you should be able to:

2.1   Describe what constitutes a crystal and how this is different from other, non-crystalline materials.

2.2   Explain, with appropriate examples, the meaning of the terms phase, stability field, and phase transformation

2.3   Identify stability fields and measure phase transformation pressures and/or temperatures, using a phase diagram.

2.4   Explain the meaning of the terms lattice, unit cell, and motif.

2.5   Give examples of different kinds of symmetry elements, and suggest examples of how they may appear at a microscopic and macroscopic level.

2.6   Outline how a crystal structure with billions of atoms can be represented concisely.

2.7   Explain what is meant by a crystal system, and how this may affect the shape of a single crystal.

2.8   Describe what is meant by a close-packed structure, and suggest materials that have such structures.

2.9   Define the term interstice, give examples of different kinds of interstice in close-packed structures, and show how filling these interstices accounts for the structures of some ionic crystals.

2.10   Give an account of different kinds of defect that may exist in a mineral structure, and suggest ways in which they may modify a mineral's physical properties.

2.11   Define the terms lustre, cleavage, hardness, and density. Explain, with examples, how each property is related to crystal structure.

Now try the following questions to test your understanding of Section 2.

Question 2.1   Using the phase diagram illustrated in Figure 2.2, determine: (a) the pressure at which water would boil at a temperature of 50 °C; and (b) the pressure and temperature at which solid ice, liquid water and gaseous steam could coexist.

Question 2.2   A new mineral has been discovered which grows in long, needle-like shapes. What crystal system can this mineral *not* belong to?

Question 2.3   On testing, an unidentified mineral was found to scratch window glass, but was itself scratched by a hardened steel file. What is the hardness of this mineral?

3 Crystal optics

Earth Sciences laboratories are using increasingly expensive and sophisticated equipment (Box 3.1) to study minerals and rocks. One basic item of equipment remains in even the most state-of-the-art lab: the optical microscope. Crystal optics may be one of the oldest analytical techniques in mineralogy, but an understanding of the way in which light interacts with crystal lattices makes it one of the most sensitive techniques available. It is also one of the simplest and most practical ways of studying the behaviour of minerals in rocks, which is why we have provided you with an optical microscope in your Home Kit.

Box 3.1 Minerals in the laboratory

If you visit any major Earth Sciences research department, you might find that most of the building is filled with bulky laboratory equipment. Earth Sciences is now very much an experimental science. Some of the major items of equipment might include:

X-ray diffraction facilities   Although we cannot 'see' the atoms inside a crystal directly, we can infer their arrangement, by analysing clues when a crystal is placed in a beam of X-rays. Because a crystalline material has a regular, repeating structure, it will cause a characteristic disturbance in the radiation, which is said to have been diffracted by the crystal. Although a detailed knowledge of crystal structure determination is beyond the scope of this course, diffraction is commonly used as a very effective way of 'fingerprinting' mineral species, and distinguishing one type of crystal from another.

Electron microprobe   If a crystal is exposed to an intense beam of electrons, its atoms will absorb some of the energy from the electron beam, and also emit X-ray radiation. By measuring the wavelengths of the X-rays emitted by the mineral, it is possible to determine which elements are present – and hence determine the mineral's chemical composition. This is a very popular technique because it is non-destructive, unlike traditional tests involving chemical reactions.

Transmission electron microscope   This is the undisputed king of all microscopes. Optical microscopes cannot resolve details finer than the wavelength of visible light (approximately 500 nm). Atoms are thousands of times smaller and, to be able to resolve atoms inside crystal lattices, we require a far more sensitive instrument. The transmission electron microscope uses radiation with a wavelength even smaller than the size of atoms – so it can peer inside crystals at very high magnifications.

3.1 The nature of light

Light is a form of **electromagnetic radiation** – and is only a small part of the whole electromagnetic spectrum, which also includes X-rays, ultraviolet and infrared radiation, and microwaves. The wavelengths of visible light span the region of the electromagnetic spectrum from about 400 nm (violet) to about 700 nm (red). Some of the properties of waves, with which you may already be familiar, are summarized in Box 3.2.

Box 3.2 Revision of waves

A wave is a disturbance that varies periodically with time, and which transports energy from one place to another. As a wave moves through space, its oscillations describe a regular sequence of peaks and troughs (like spreading ripples on a pond, but in three dimensions). The number of wave peaks that pass a fixed point per second is called the wave's frequency. The distance between successive peaks is called the wavelength, and depends on both the frequency of the oscillation, and the speed of propagation of the wave:

$$\text{wavelength} = \text{speed}/\text{frequency}$$

(Note that the speed of propagation of the wave generally depends on the nature of the medium through which the wave travels – e.g., the speed of sound in air is different from the speed of sound in water.)

The oscillating nature of a wave is analogous to the hand of a clock moving round (Figure 3.1). The angle through which the hand has swept is equivalent to the phase of the wave, and is represented by the Greek symbol ϕ (phi).

Mathematically, the displacement of a wave, A, at any instant is given by a cosine formula:

$$A = A_0 \cos \phi$$

where A_0 is the maximum displacement, or amplitude, of the wave.

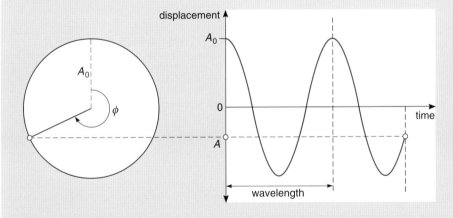

Figure 3.1   A representation of how a wave (in blue) can be modelled as the hand of a clock sweeping round through the angle ϕ. The displacement, A, of the wave from the horizontal is given by $A_0 \cos \phi$; the angle ϕ is called the phase angle.

A single ray of light is actually two oscillating fields: an electric field and a magnetic field. The planes of oscillation for the electric and magnetic components are at right angles to each other, and to the direction of propagation of the radiation, as illustrated in Figure 3.2. For simplicity, we shall focus on the oscillating electric field, and ignore the magnetic field.

Figure 3.2   (a) Representation of light as oscillating electric and magnetic fields, arranged at 90° to each other. (b) In a polarized beam of light, the oscillating electric field is confined to a single plane. (c) Unpolarized light shows a range of different orientations of the electric field.

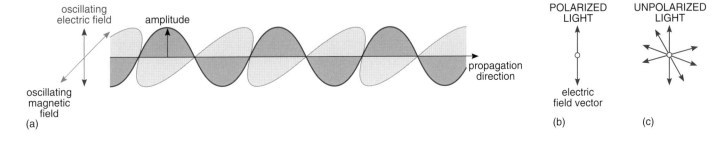

The plane containing the oscillating electric field is called the **plane of polarization** of the ray. In general, a beam of light will contain many such rays, and their planes of polarization will be oriented differently. If we wish to use light as a sensitive probe, we need to have some control over the planes of polarization. One way of achieving this is to use a special polarizing filter, or polarizer, which allows only one plane of polarization through (Figure 3.3); the transmitted light is called **plane-polarized light**. We have included two polarizing filters in your Home Kit – sheets of Polaroid.

Figure 3.3 The production of plane-polarized light by passing a beam of unpolarized light through a polarizing filter.

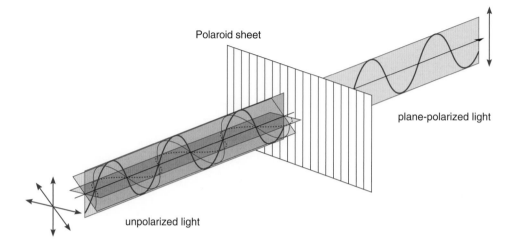

3.2 THE INTERACTION OF LIGHT AND MATTER

What happens when light passes *through* a crystal? When so many minerals are apparently transparent and colourless, it seems difficult to believe that there can be any interaction between crystal and light, but examples from everyday life suggest otherwise. If you shine a torch at night, or drive a car with headlights on, the light fades with distance. This is an example of interaction between light and matter. The energy of the light is being progressively absorbed by the molecules in air. (In a vacuum, light can travel unimpeded – just as starlight reaches us from stars that are thousands of light years distant.) Compared with the gases that make up the atmosphere, crystals are very dense materials, so we might expect light to be much more strongly absorbed in a crystal than it is in air. This is just one of the interactions that takes place between crystals and light. We shall also be investigating some other interactions that allow us to probe sensitive aspects of crystal structures.

3.2.1 COLOUR

When we talk about light passing through a crystal, we are generally referring to white light, which contains a spread of wavelengths from red to violet. The extent to which the light is absorbed in a crystal may well vary with wavelength. The loss, or attenuation, of some wavelengths from the light emerging from a crystal results in the crystal appearing coloured.

If we shine plane-polarized light through a crystal, the electric field associated with the light will be vibrating parallel to a specific direction in the crystal. If we were to rotate the crystal relative to the transmitted light, this direction would change. The electric field associated with the light might then be interacting with a different arrangement of atoms. For some crystals, the variation of these atomic arrangements with direction is great enough to affect the crystal's colour. For example, a very thin slice of biotite (a common rock-forming mineral) viewed in transmitted plane-polarized light may show a faint yellow colour. This gradually changes to brown as the slice is rotated about an axis parallel to the direction of the light. This property of colour variation is called **pleochroism**.

3.2.2 REFRACTIVE INDEX

All crystals contain atoms, which have electrons, and these contribute to a strong internal electric field. Such a field will interact with the oscillating electric field of light passing through the crystal. A major effect of this interaction is to slow down the passage of light through a crystal: the stronger the electric field in the crystal, the slower the light. This effect is measured by the **refractive index**, which is the ratio of the speed of light in a vacuum to the speed of light in the crystal:

$$\text{refractive index} = \frac{\text{speed of light in vacuum}^*}{\text{speed of light in crystal}}$$

As you have seen, different directions in a crystal generally have different arrangements of atoms. So a ray of light whose plane of polarization is oriented one way in the crystal will experience a different electric field compared with a ray with its plane of polarization oriented differently. In other words, the two rays will travel through the crystal at different speeds and they will experience different refractive indices.

3.2.3 ANISOTROPY OF REFRACTIVE INDEX

Non-crystalline materials, such as window glass, do not show any appreciable structural variation with direction (the atomic arrangements are randomly oriented in all directions). Their physical properties are also independent of direction, and these materials are described as being **isotropic**. In contrast, many crystals show large contrasts in atomic arrangement in different directions. Their physical properties may also vary with direction, and these materials are referred to as being **anisotropic**. Most crystals are anisotropic; the exceptions to this are cubic crystals, which are isotropic. The reason for this will be explained shortly.

We've already seen that the absorption of light can vary with direction, giving rise to pleochroism. Refractive index may also vary with direction, and it does so in a smooth manner. We can represent this variation by drawing a three-dimensional ellipsoid, whose orientation is fixed relative to the crystal (Figure 3.4). The relative magnitude of the refractive index for light vibrating along any direction is simply the length of an arrow from the centre of the ellipsoid, to its surface (e.g., the lines OP and OQ in Figure 3.4). This ellipsoid is called the **optical indicatrix** for the crystal.

The optical indicatrix is a fundamental property of a crystal structure, ultimately determined by the atomic arrangements. Hence, the shape and orientation of the indicatrix must be consistent with the crystal symmetry.

Crystal systems with a single three-, four- or six-fold rotation axis (i.e. trigonal, tetragonal or hexagonal) impose constraints on the shape of the indicatrix, requiring it to have one circular cross-section, at right angles to the rotational axis of the crystal. The indicatrix is therefore an ellipsoid-of-revolution (i.e. it can be made by rotating an ellipse about one of its axes), illustrated in Figure 3.5c. The direction at right angles to the circular cross-section is called the optic axis and has very special optical properties, which we shall investigate later.

The cubic system imposes more constraints on the shape of the indicatrix. There are four three-fold axes, so our ellipsoid must have at least four circular sections. The only shape possible is a sphere (Figure 3.5d). Thus, a cubic crystal has the

* As a standard, the velocity of light in a vacuum is taken as 1 and other light velocities related to this; since the velocity of light in air = 0.9997, this is also generally taken as 1.

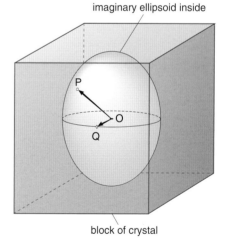

imaginary ellipsoid inside

block of crystal

Figure 3.4   The variation of refractive index with direction in a crystal, represented by the length of a line from the centre of an ellipsoid to its surface. Consider plane-polarized light passing through a block of crystal such that its plane of polarization is parallel to the line OP; the magnitude of the refractive index affecting the light is then given by the length of the line OP. It would be different from that of light passing through parallel to the line OQ.

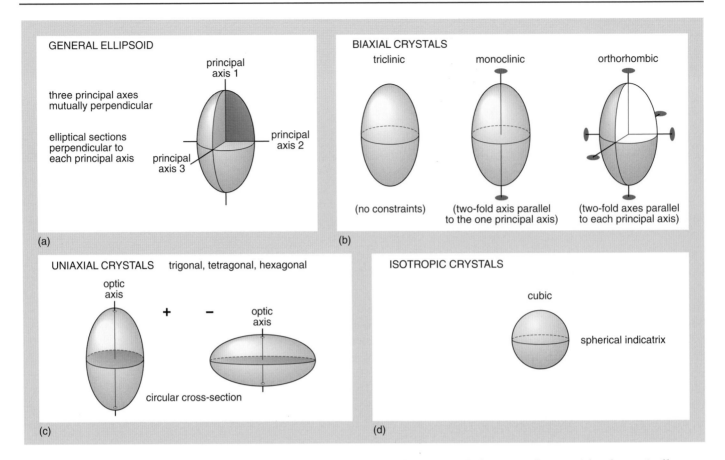

Figure 3.5 Shapes of the optical indicatrix for different crystal systems. (a) An ellipsoid is a three-dimensional shape with elliptical cross-sections – each of which has two-fold rotational symmetry. (b) Low-symmetry crystal systems place no constraints on the *shape* of the indicatrix, only its orientation (the two-fold symmetry of the ellipsoid must line up with any two-fold symmetry in the crystal). (c) For trigonal, tetragonal and hexagonal crystals, the ellipsoid must have one circular cross-section, perpendicular to the three-fold, four-fold or six-fold axis. These crystals are called *uniaxial crystals*, and may be optically positive or negative, as indicated by the plus and minus signs. (d) Cubic crystals have spherical indicatrices.

same refractive index in all directions. Cubic crystals are said to be optically isotropic. This is in contrast to all other crystal systems, which show some variation in optical properties (i.e., refractive index) for different directions in their crystals. These crystals are said to be optically anisotropic.

From our discussion of the shape of the optical indicatrix, we can divide anisotropic crystals into two groups. Crystals with no more than two-fold rotational symmetry (i.e., triclinic, monoclinic or orthorhombic systems) are said to be **biaxial** (it turns out that the optical indicatrices for these crystals have *two* circular cross-sections). Crystals with more than two-fold rotational symmetry (i.e., trigonal, tetragonal or hexagonal) are said to be **uniaxial** (the indicatrix has only *one* circular cross-section). We can further subdivide uniaxial crystals, according to whether the indicatrix is stretched out parallel to the optic axis, into the shape of a rugby ball (optically positive), or whether it is squashed in this direction, into a 'Smartie' or 'burger' shape (optically negative) (Figure 3.5c).

3.2.4 DOUBLE REFRACTION

Anisotropic crystals have a surprising and, indeed, remarkable property: when plane-polarized light enters such a crystal it becomes split into two rays. The explanation for this involves complex crystal physics, which is beyond the scope of this course. Nevertheless, the consequences are profound. The two rays are both plane-polarized, but their planes of polarization (i.e., their vibration directions) are at 90° to each other. This means that the two rays will encounter different atomic arrangements with different refractive indices, and will therefore travel at different speeds through the crystal. If the refractive indices are very different (that is, if the crystal has a very high **birefringence**), then the two rays will be *refracted* to very different extents, and it may be possible to view two distinct images, one from each ray. This effect is called **double refraction**; (Figure 3.6).

❑   Would you expect to see double refraction in a cubic crystal?

■   No. Cubic crystals are isotropic. Double refraction occurs only in anisotropic crystals.

Activity 3.1

One of the best illustrations of double refraction is provided by the mineral calcite. In this Activity, you will observe double refraction from a calcite crystal and investigate the polarization of the two rays of light as they emerge from the crystal.

3.3 MINERALS IN THIN SECTION

We have seen that anisotropic crystals can split light into two rays, which travel at different speeds through the crystal. For very thick and highly anisotropic crystals such as your calcite rhomb, we can see the double refraction, and sample the polarization of the two rays using Polaroid sheets. However, mostly we'll be dealing with very thin slices, or sections, of minerals (about 0.03 mm thick) for which no such double refraction is visible. How, then, can we detect the double refraction? To answer this, we need to look in more detail at what happens when the two rays pass through a thin section of crystal.

You may find Sections 3.3.1 to 3.3.3 rather difficult. We are trying to explain the physics behind an extremely useful optical property of crystals. If this is beyond you please do not worry. However, it is important that you take note of the final paragraph of Section 3.3.3, perform Activity 3.2, and are then able to follow the text from Section 3.3.4 onwards.

3.3.1 PERMITTED VIBRATION DIRECTIONS

We can determine the refractive indices experienced by the two rays, and their vibration directions, using the optical indicatrix (Figure 3.7). We take the section of the indicatrix that is perpendicular to the light direction (which will be either a circle or an ellipse), and identify its principal axes (i.e., the long axis and the short axis of the ellipse). This defines the two **permitted vibration directions** for the two rays of light inside the crystal.

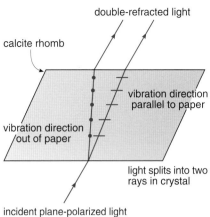

Figure 3.6   Side-view through a calcite cleavage rhomb, showing how light is doubly refracted into two rays as it passes through the crystal. For calcite, the refractive indices of the two rays are very different, so the two rays are refracted through different angles and travel along different paths through the crystal.

Figure 3.7   Determining the permitted vibration directions for light in a crystal, using the optical indicatrix. (a) A diagram showing the cross-section of the indicatrix perpendicular to the incident light. (b) The view from above, into the light beam, showing the permitted vibration directions for the two rays. (c) The refractive indices experienced by the two rays are in the ratio of the two principal axes of the ellipse, e_1 and e_2.

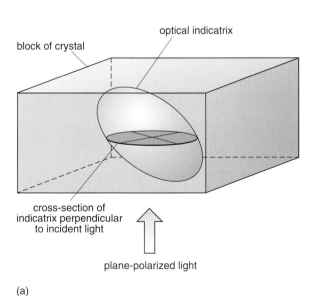

(a)

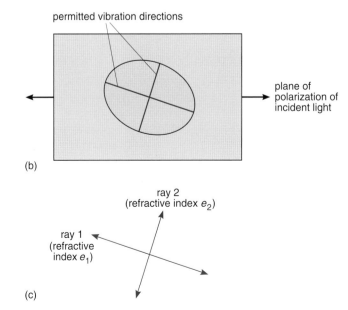

(b)

(c)

If the permitted vibration directions are at some arbitrary angle to the polarization direction of the incident light, then light entering the crystal will be split into two rays, whose planes of polarization will be parallel to the e_1 and e_2 directions (Figure 3.7b and c).

❑   What happens if the thin section is rotated slightly from the position shown in Figure 3.7b, so that one vibration direction (say, the e_1 direction) is exactly parallel to the plane of polarization of the incident light?

■   The ray of light would not split into two rays. The single ray would pass through the crystal with its plane of polarization parallel to the polarizer direction. The ray would experience only the refractive index e_1.

3.3.2   TWO RAYS, TWO SPEEDS

Do you remember how we described a ray of light? Light includes an oscillating electric field, which is a wave. When a ray of light first enters an anisotropic crystal it splits into two rays, and at this point their oscillations are exactly in step with each other. The two rays are said to have a phase difference of zero (illustrated in Figure 3.8a).

However, the two rays emerge from the crystal with a phase difference, because they've been slowed down by different amounts (Figure 3.9 and Box 3.3).

The phase difference depends on three factors (Equation 3.2):

1   the thickness of the crystal, d;

2   the difference between the two refractive indices, $e_1 - e_2$ (which depends on how anisotropic the material is): this is called the birefringence of the crystal;

3   the wavelength of the light in air, λ.

If we could combine these two rays, the properties of the resulting ray would carry very useful information about the optical properties of the crystal.

❑   Why don't the two rays combine (add) inside the crystal?

■   The two rays are plane polarized, and their planes of polarization are at 90° to each other – so they act independently of each other, and cannot be added.

Even when the two rays emerge from the crystal, they are still plane polarized at 90° to each other, and are independent.

Figure 3.8   The addition of two waves. The upper figures show individual waves 1 and 2; the lower figures show the sums of the amplitudes of the two waves. (a) The two waves are in step: their phase difference is zero. (b) The two waves are exactly out of step (by one-half of the wavelength): their phase difference is 180°. Because the two waves have the same amplitude but are out of phase, their sum is zero (so the two waves exactly cancel each other out). (c) The two waves are partly out of step: phase difference is ϕ. The sum is a wave with the same frequency as the original waves, but out of phase with both of them.

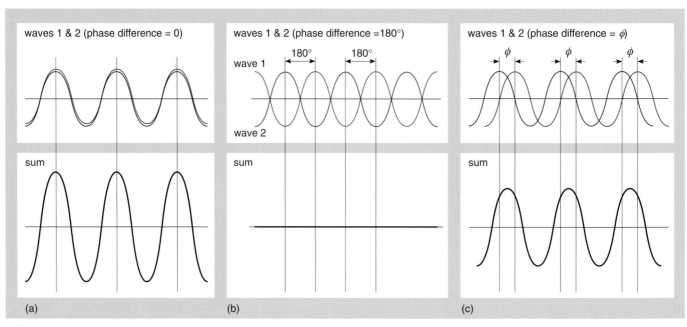

Box 3.3 The origin of phase difference

Figure 3.9 shows two rays of light leaving a crystal with the same wavelength, but having travelled at different speeds through the crystal because they are vibrating in different directions. Thus, in the time it takes the *slower* of the two rays (i.e., the one experiencing the larger refractive index, e_1) to travel through the crystal, the faster ray (experiencing the smaller refractive index, e_2) has already passed through the crystal and travelled an extra distance in the air. This **optical path difference**, denoted by the Greek letter delta, Δ, is called the retardation.

If the crystal has a thickness d, then remembering our definition of refractive index on page 29, we can write:

$$\text{time} = \text{distance}/\text{speed}$$

$$\text{time taken for slow ray to pass through crystal} = t_1 = d\frac{e_1}{c}$$

$$\text{time taken for fast ray to pass through crystal} = t_2 = d\frac{e_2}{c}$$

(where c is the speed of light in air). So, the extra distance, Δ, covered by the fast ray in time $t_1 - t_2$ is:

$$\text{distance} = \text{speed} \times \text{time}$$

$$= \text{speed of light in air} \times (t_1 - t_2)$$

$$= = c\left\{\frac{de_1}{c} - \frac{de_2}{c}\right\} = d\{e_1 - e_2\}$$

So the retardation is $\Delta = d(e_1 - e_2)$ (3.1)

Now, the number of wavelengths represented by this distance is just Δ/λ (where λ is the wavelength of the light in air), so the difference in phase, ϕ, (Figure 3.8c) between the two rays is:

$$\phi = \frac{\Delta}{\lambda} \times 360°$$

$$= \frac{d}{\lambda}\{e_1 - e_2\} \times 360° \qquad (3.2)$$

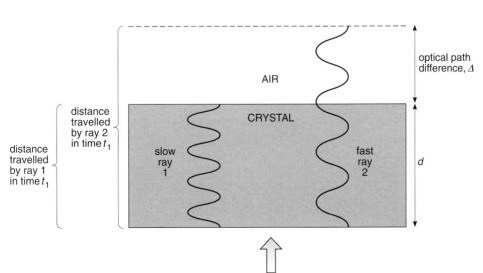

Figure 3.9 The origin of the phase difference between two rays passing through a crystal. A ray of light with wavelength λ splits into two rays as it enters a crystal. If the two rays travel at different speeds through the same thickness of crystal, then when the slow ray emerges from the crystal after time t_1, it will be lagging behind the fast ray – and there will be an optical path difference between the two rays.

optical path difference, Δ

AIR

CRYSTAL

distance travelled by ray 2 in time t_1

distance travelled by ray 1 in time t_1

slow ray 1

fast ray 2

d

light (wavelength λ)

3.3.3 Reuniting the two rays

We can combine the two rays by using a special optical trick: we pass them through another sheet of Polaroid, called an analyser. The analyser is aligned so that it will only pass light whose plane of polarization is perpendicular to the polarizer vibration direction; that is, it is *crossed* relative to the polarizer. In this relative position, the two sheets are referred to as **crossed polars**.

❑ If there were no crystal in between, would you expect any light to be passed when the analyser is at 90° to the polarizer?

■ No. (You can verify this using the two Polaroid sheets in the Home Kit; hold them up against the light and rotate one sheet so that its allowed vibration direction is at 90° to the other sheet.)

Now let's consider what will happen if we place a crystal between the analyser and polarizer, as illustrated in Figure 3.10a. A ray of light entering the crystal will split into two rays. The two rays will be parallel to the e_1 and e_2 directions (Figure 3.10b and Figure 3.11a), which are inclined with respect to both the analyser and the polarizer vibration directions. The two rays travel at different speeds through the crystal, and when they emerge there is a phase difference between them (as shown in Box 3.3).

Figure 3.10 Viewing a crystal between crossed polars. (a) Side view showing the crystal placed between two Polaroid sheets, the analyser and the polarizer. (b) Plan view showing a crystal slice, with the appropriate cross-section of the indicatrix superimposed, and the polarizer and analyser vibration directions marked for reference. The e_1 vibration direction of this crystal slice is inclined at an angle θ (Greek theta) to the analyser vibration direction.

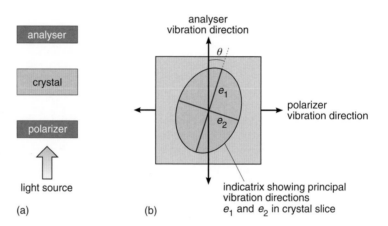

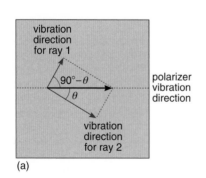
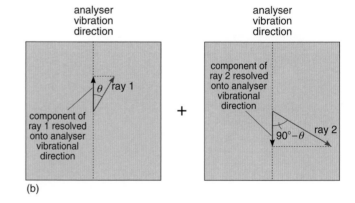

Figure 3.11 The progress of plane-polarized light through a crystal.
(a) A plane-polarized ray splits into two when it enters the crystal; the two rays (1 and 2) vibrate parallel to the crystal slice's principal vibration directions (e_1 and e_2, respectively), which are at angles of $90° - \theta$ and θ to the polarizer vibration direction, respectively.
(b) The two rays emerge from the crystal, and are combined in the analyser. The analyser will only transmit light vibrating parallel to its vibration direction; because the vibration directions for the two rays are inclined to the analyser direction (at angles of θ and $90° - \theta$, respectively), only a component of each ray is passed through the analyser (see Box 3.4).

The analyser transmits light that is polarized parallel to the analyser vibration direction. The two rays shown in Figure 3.11a therefore cannot be transmitted in their entirety. However, this does not mean that no light at all will be transmitted. Remember what happened when plane-polarized light entered the crystal. We said that the ray was split into two components, which were parallel to the crystal's vibration directions. We say that the ray was *resolved* onto the e_1 and e_2 directions.

Something similar happens at the analyser. A ray with its electric field vibrating parallel to the e_1 direction (ray 1 in Figure 3.11) is resolved into two components, one in the analyser vibration direction and one at right angles to it. Only the former component passes through the analyser to the viewer. Similarly, ray 2 is resolved into two components, only one of which passes through the analyser. The total amount of light passed by the analyser is the sum of the two resolved electric field components oscillating in the analyser vibration direction (Figure 3.11b).

Figure 3.11b shows that, when $\theta = 45°$, the component of ray 1 resolved onto the analyser direction is equal and opposite to the component of ray 2 resolved onto the analyser direction, and one might expect them to cancel out. What has happened is that resolving the two rays onto the analyser direction has resulted in a phase difference of 180° between the two components (Figure 3.8b). What Figure 3.11 *doesn't* show, however, is that there is a slight phase difference, ϕ, between rays 1 and 2, caused by their different speeds in the crystal. This means that, in the analyser, the resolved components will have a phase difference of $180° - \phi$: they will not cancel out, and some light will be transmitted.

To summarize, light is passed by the analyser only when the two rays emerging from the crystal have a non-zero phase difference.

For a given crystal, cut into a thin slice in a specific orientation, the phase difference between the two rays is fixed: it can't be varied. However, we can rotate the crystal slice so that its permitted vibration directions are at different angles to the polarizer vibration direction (i.e., we can vary the angle θ in Figure 3.11).

❑   What would happen if one of the crystal's permitted vibration directions was exactly parallel to the polarizer direction?

■   Light entering the crystal would experience only one refractive index – and would not split into two rays. The plane of polarization would be parallel to the polarizer direction, and at 90° to the analyser direction. It would therefore be blocked by the analyser, and so the crystal would appear dark.

Whenever one of the crystal's permitted vibration directions is parallel to the polarizer direction, no light will be passed through the analyser. In other words, when the crystal's e_1 direction is at 0°, 90°, 180° or 270° to the polarizer (i.e., four times per complete rotation of the crystal), the crystal will appear dark – and is said to be in **extinction**. In between these positions (45°, 135°, 225°, 315°), the crystal will appear bright. In fact, we commonly refer to the **45° position** as the position in which a crystal appears the brightest.

Activity 3.2

This has been a long and difficult Section. However, we hope that you now understand the origins of the dark/bright contrast seen when an anisotropic crystal is rotated between crossed polars. Activity 3.2 allows you to put these concepts into practice, by experimenting with a polarizer, an analyser, and a thin section of crystal.

Box 3.4 Resolving components

Figure 3.12 shows an example of a vibrating system (a truck moving backwards and forwards along a railway track), viewed from different angles, to illustrate how oscillation along one direction can be perceived, or *resolved*, along another direction.

In Figure 3.12a, the oscillation is at 90° to the viewer's plane of vision (the dashed line down the page), and would not be visible to the viewer. In Figure 3.12b the oscillation is parallel to the plane of vision, and the extent of the oscillation perceived by the viewer, *l*, is the same as the actual oscillation, *d*. Figure 3.12c shows a more general case where the railway track is at an angle,

θ, to the plane of vision. Some motion will be perceived by the viewer, but its extent, *l*, is less than the actual motion along the track, *d*.

In summary, the amount of motion that is perceived by the viewer depends on the actual extent of oscillation, *d*, and the angle, θ, between the oscillation direction (the railway track), and the viewer's plane of vision. Mathematically, this is expressed as:

$$l = d \cos \theta$$

where *l* represents the oscillation *resolved* onto the plane of vision.

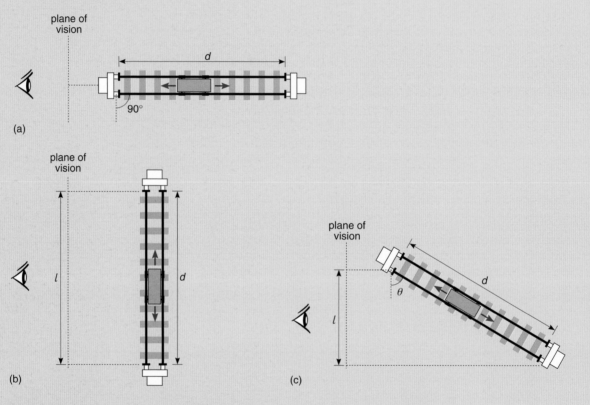

Figure 3.12   An oscillating system, and how the motion perceived depends on the angle of view. (a) Viewed end-on, the truck has no apparent motion; (b) viewed side-on at 90° the truck's apparent motion, *l*, is the same as its actual motion, *d*; (c) viewed side-on at an angle θ, the apparent motion is given by $l = d \cos \theta$. The length *l* is the component of the actual motion *d* resolved onto the direction of the plane of vision.

3.3.4 INTERFERENCE COLOURS

In Activity 3.2, you saw how an anisotropic crystal allowed light to pass through two crossed Polaroid sheets – and that without the crystal, no light could pass at all. As the crystal was rotated relative to the sheets, the intensity of the light passed varied from bright, to completely dark.

You may have noticed another feature of the crystal seen between crossed polars: it showed a distinctive colour (or maybe a range of colours), perhaps yellow–

pink. This colour was not caused by the crystal itself being coloured (the crystal slice was colourless and transparent!), but was produced by viewing between crossed polars. The colour is referred to as an **interference colour** – because it is related to the process of combining two rays of light from the crystal in the analyser. So far, our discussion of polarized light has assumed monochromatic light (light of a single wavelength) – whereas you were looking at the crystal in white light (a spread of wavelengths from red to blue).

We have seen that, for monochromatic light, the intensity (brightness) of the light passed depends on the orientation of the crystal relative to the analyser and polarizer directions. Now let's consider what happens if we keep the orientation of the crystal fixed (say in the 45° position), but vary its thickness.

❑ In what way does an increase in the crystal's thickness affect the phase difference between the two rays of light emerging from the crystal?

◼ The phase difference increases with an increase in thickness (there is a linear relation between the two, as shown in Equation 3.2 in Box 3.3).

Gradually increasing the thickness of a crystal is equivalent to gradually increasing the phase difference between the two rays of light. With no crystal (zero thickness!) there would be no phase difference.

❑ How does the phase difference between the two rays relate to the amount of light passed by the analyser?

◼ If the phase difference is zero, the resolved components of the two rays exactly cancel each other out in the analyser. Light is passed only if there is a phase difference.

So, increasing the thickness of a crystal increases the phase difference, causing the crystal to appear brighter – but only up to a point ... Remember, a phase difference of 360°, or any multiple of 360°, is the same as a phase difference of 0°, which, as we've already established, results in no light being passed through the analyser. So, thicker and thicker crystals would appear brighter, then darker, then brighter, and so on (complete darkness at phase differences of 0°, 360° ... and maximum brightness at phase differences of 180°, 540° ...).

We don't need to keep switching crystals to see the effect of changing thickness: a wedge-shaped piece of crystal gives us a continuous range of thicknesses, depending on the angle of the wedge.

❑ What will be the appearance of a crystal wedge between crossed polars (assuming that it is in the 45° position)?

◼ The thinnest end of the wedge will be dark, then as we move up the wedge to greater thicknesses, a pattern of bright and dark bands (called fringes) will be seen.

❑ What would happen if we were to increase the angle of the wedge?

◼ A given point on the wedge would now correspond to a greater thickness of crystal. We would therefore see more bands along the wedge, and the separation between the bands would be smaller – i.e., the bands would appear to move closer together.

Figure 3.13a summarizes what would be seen for crystal wedges with different wedge angles.

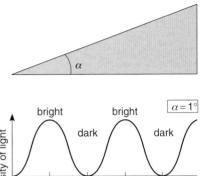
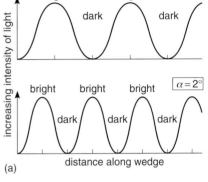

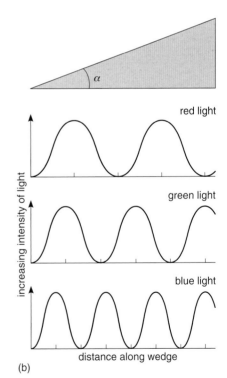

Figure 3.13 The variation in the intensity of light transmitted through a crystal wedge, viewed between crossed polars. (a) Increasing the angle of the wedge forces the bright and dark bands closer together. (b) Reducing the wavelength of the light, from red to green to blue, forces the bright and dark bands closer together. (c) Combining red, green, and blue light (as white light) results in a scale of colours (see also Plate 3.1).

Now let's see what happens when we change the wavelength of the light.

❑ Using Equation 3.2, what would you expect to happen to the bright and dark bands along the crystal wedge, if we were to reduce the wavelength, λ?

■ Reducing the wavelength increases the phase difference, and is equivalent to increasing the thickness of the crystal. For our wedge, this is equivalent to increasing the wedge angle, α, and we've already seen that this would result in the bright and dark bands moving closer together.

We can now begin to build up a picture of what might happen for different wavelengths of light passing through varying thicknesses of a crystal. At different points along the wedge, different wavelengths of light will be completely cut out (Figure 3.13b). If we were to combine all the wavelengths, as white light, then we would see a scale of colours along the wedge (Figure 3.13c): this is called **Newton's scale of colours** – and is depicted on the **Michel–Levy chart** in Plate 3.1.

Activity 3.3

The origin of interference colour is probably the most difficult concept you'll meet in this part of the course. You can experiment with interference colours and crystal wedges using the 'Virtual Lightbox', in this DVD Activity.

3.3.5 MEASURING INTERFERENCE COLOURS

The Michel–Levy chart is a depiction of the interference colours seen on a wedge of quartz crystal. We can use this as a guide to the interference colours from other mineral specimens. The colour scale can be divided into a series of colour ranges, or 'orders', each separated by a bright pink band. Colours towards the darker (thin) end of the wedge are called 'low order' colours, and colours at the lighter (thick) end of the wedge are called 'high order' colours. So, with increasing phase difference between the two rays, we get higher-order interference colours.

❑ Place the gypsum section (TS X) from your Home Kit between crossed Polaroid sheets, in its 45° position, and compare its interference colour with those shown on the Michel–Levy chart.

■ The colour seen should be yellow to pink, but could belong to any order. Note, however, that with increasing order, the colours become progressively washed-out. The strongest, most vivid colours are in the first and second orders, and your gypsum section shows a first-order colour.

Note that the amount of phase difference – expressed in terms of the optical path difference (retardation) – is given at the bottom of the chart, in nanometres. You can directly relate the observed interference colour to the retardation.

❑ Use the Michel–Levy chart to determine the retardation of your gypsum crystal.

■ The gypsum sections have been prepared with a thickness of approximately 30 μm, which gives first-order yellow-to-pink colours, corresponding to a retardation of about 550 nm.

Knowing the thickness of a section and its retardation, we can calculate its birefringence, that is, the numerical difference between the two refractive indices of the crystal section. All thin sections have a standard thickness of 30 μm, and retardation can be found by matching the interference colour on the Michel–Levy chart and reading off the retardation value. The birefringence is calculated (rearranging Equation 3.1) as:

birefringence = retardation/thickness

Question 3.1   What is the birefringence of your gypsum section?

When looking at other crystals, it is important to be aware of possible ambiguity in using the Michel–Levy chart. Some colours – particularly yellows to oranges – appear in several places (i.e., different orders) on the chart. Sometimes it can be difficult to determine the corresponding order of a particular interference colour. It may be possible to determine the order by looking at the edge of a grain, which is often thinner than the centre; as such, it behaves like a built-in wedge, and coloured fringes may be seen. In general, higher-order colours appear much more washed-out and pastel-like than lower-order colours, which are brighter and more vivid.

3.3.6 MAXIMUM BIREFRINGENCE

❏   If we were to take a single crystal of a mineral and slice it into differently oriented sections, we'd almost certainly observe a different interference colour for each section – even if the sections were of the same thickness. Why is this?

■   Interference colour, observed between crossed polars, is affected by the birefringence of the section. But birefringence will be different for crystal slices that were cut in different orientations – as we saw from the optical indicatrix (Figure 3.7).

If you look at a section containing many differently oriented crystals of the same mineral, it should be possible to use the Michel–Levy chart to find the **maximum interference colour**. This corresponds to the greatest refractive index difference in the crystal (i.e., the largest birefringence) – and is characteristic of the mineral being examined (maximum birefringences for common minerals are tabulated in many mineral reference books).

❏   Look at thin section (TS) A from your Home Kit between the two Polaroid sheets, holding them up to the light. This rock contains just quartz crystals – all in different orientations. What is the maximum interference colour for quartz, and where does this lie on the Michel–Levy chart?

■   The colours should vary from dark grey to yellowish-white (the maximum interference colour). These colours occur only in the first order.

3.3.7 BIREFRINGENCE AND CRYSTAL STRUCTURE

Throughout this Block, we have stressed the relationship between crystal properties and crystal structure. Continuing in this vein, we can relate birefringence to crystal structure, taking the mineral calcite as an example.

You met calcite in Activity 3.1, where you saw that it had such high anisotropy that *double refraction* was clearly evident. We can explain the origins of this bizarre phenomenon by looking for signs of anisotropy in calcite's crystal structure.

The calcite structure contains planes of carbonate groups, $(CO_3)^{2-}$, separated by calcium ions, Ca^{2+}. Large numbers of electrons *within* each carbonate plane contribute to a very high electric field (Figure 3.14a). A ray of polarized light whose vibration direction is parallel to a carbonate plane will be strongly affected by the crystal's electric field (that is, the refractive index in this direction is very *high*), and the end result is that its speed will be greatly reduced.

However, there are far fewer electrons arranged at *right angles* to the carbonate planes, so the crystal's electric field is much weaker in this direction (that is, the refractive index for this direction is very *low*). Therefore, a ray of light whose vibration direction is at right angles to the carbonate planes will not be significantly slowed down (Figure 3.14a).

Figure 3.14 The origin of anisotropy in calcite. (a) Part of the calcite structure, showing layers of $(CO_3)^{2-}$ groups, separated by Ca^{2+} ions. The many electrons within the $(CO_3)^{2-}$ layers create a strong electric field, so that light vibrating parallel to the layers will be slowed down. By contrast, there is a much weaker electric field perpendicular to the layers. (b) Fast and slow vibration directions for light travelling out of the paper. (c) A cross-section of the indicatrix for this orientation, showing the large difference in the two principal refractive indices, e_1 and e_2, for the two permitted vibration directions.

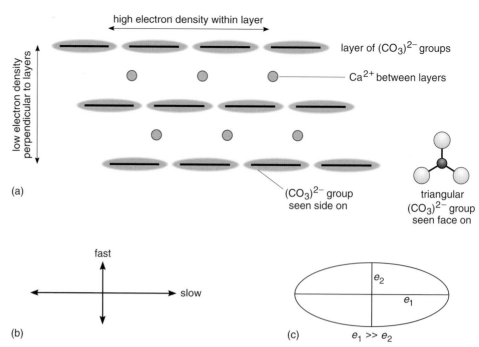

If a calcite crystal is oriented so that light splits into two directions, one parallel to the carbonate planes, and one at right angles to the planes (Figure 3.14b), then the two rays will experience very different refractive indices (Figure 3.14c), and consequently travel at very different speeds through the crystal. Thus, calcite can show very high birefringence.

Anisotropy is not always restricted to crystalline materials. It can also be seen in non-crystalline materials that have been subjected to stress – as explored in the next Activity.

Activity 3.4

This Activity demonstrates the correlation between anisotropy and interference colour, using the alignment of polymer molecules in a plastic sheet as an example. Most unstressed plastics have a random arrangement of polymer molecules, and so are optically isotropic. Stretching a plastic sheet pulls the long polymer molecules into alignment, creating anisotropy in the structure – and effectively turning the plastic into a two-dimensional crystal.

3.4 PRACTICAL ASPECTS OF CRYSTAL OPTICS

3.4.1 INTRODUCTION TO THE POLARIZING MICROSCOPE

The polarizing microscope looks very similar to an ordinary microscope (such as that used for looking at biological specimens). The only differences are that it contains two Polaroid sheets (just like the ones you used earlier), and that it has a rotatable stage. Figure 3.15 illustrates the layout of your polarizing microscope. Plane-polarized light is produced by passing light through a Polaroid filter (the polarizer) beneath the rotatable stage. The polarized light then passes through a thin section of a mineral, mounted on the stage. A magnified image is produced using two sets of lenses: a lower **objective lens**, and an upper, eyepiece lens. The magnification can be varied by changing the objective lens: most microscopes have a selection of different-power objective lenses. The image can be focused by moving the lens assembly up or down, using the focusing knob.

It is usual to start by looking at a thin section using plane-polarized light and low magnification. Once the specimen is correctly focused, and its important features are noted, we can use a second Polaroid filter, the analyser (located at the top of the microscope, over the eyepiece lens), to view the specimen between crossed polars (just as you viewed specimens between the two hand-held Polaroid sheets). The next two Activities show you how to put all this theory into practice.

Activity 3.5

You should now watch the first five minutes of the video sequence *Using the microscope* on DVD 1, which gives a tour of the polarizing microscope.

Activity 3.6

This Activity introduces you to using the polarizing microscope. Do this Activity now, if you have time; otherwise, you should complete it immediately before Activity 3.7.

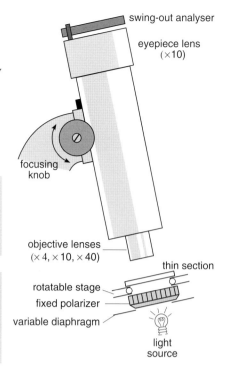

Figure 3.15 Some details of the polarizing microscope.

3.4.2 MINERAL PROPERTIES IN THIN SECTION

For the rest of the course, you will be looking at thin sections (glass slides) of *rocks*, using the polarizing microscope. Thin sections are made by glueing a slice of rock onto a glass slide, and then grinding and polishing the slice until it is thin enough for most minerals to become transparent. Usually, a standard thickness of 30 μm is chosen, to make it easier to compare different thin sections.

You can treat the thin sections as collections of minerals in different orientations. We have discussed the origins of interference colour in some detail, but there are other properties that can be used to distinguish minerals in thin section. These are explained and explored as you study the rest of this Block but, for ease of reference, the optical properties of the most common rock-forming minerals are also summarized on the Block 2 *Bookmark*.

IN PLANE-POLARIZED LIGHT

Cleavage traces may be seen as faint straight lines cutting through a mineral section. Sometimes they are parallel or perpendicular to a mineral's vibration directions – which will give **straight extinction** when viewed between crossed polars; otherwise, the mineral is said to show **inclined extinction** when viewed between crossed polars.

Relief is the term used to describe the surface appearance of a crystal in plane-polarized light. Minerals with a refractive index very different from that of the mounting glue appear to 'stand out' from the slide, and individual grain boundaries are easily seen. Any surface imperfections also appear pronounced. Low-relief minerals have refractive indices almost identical with that of the mounting glue and, because individual grain boundaries are not easily observed, the minerals are almost invisible in plane-polarized light. If the mineral is highly anisotropic, the relief may vary as you rotate the stage – as the polarized light samples first one vibration direction, then the other permitted vibration direction in the crystal section.

Opaque minerals tend to be metal oxides, such as haematite (Fe_2O_3) or ilmenite ($FeTiO_3$). Opaque minerals transmit no light – even in 30 μm thin sections. They therefore appear black in plane-polarized light (and also when seen between crossed polars in any orientation). Do not confuse opaque minerals with isotropic minerals, which appear black only between crossed polars.

Coloured minerals are often rich in iron (e.g., mafic minerals). If the colour changes as the mineral is rotated in plane-polarized light, then the mineral is said to be pleochroic (i.e. the mineral absorbs light differently in different orientations – you met this concept in Section 3.2.1). You should note the colour variation, as the mineral's pleochroic scheme. **Biotite** (brown mica) is a good example of a pleochroic mineral, with characteristic yellow–brown pleochroism.

BETWEEN CROSSED POLARS

Isotropic vs. anisotropic. Isotropic minerals belong to the cubic system and always appear black between crossed polars, regardless of their orientation (note that, unless they are opaque, isotropic minerals will transmit light when viewed in plane-polarized light). You should also recall that non-crystalline materials, such as glass, tend to be isotropic.

An anisotropic mineral will display an interference colour (unless it is an opaque mineral) when viewed between crossed polars, and will pass in and out of extinction as the stage is rotated. Note that the interference colour seen between crossed polars depends on the orientation of the mineral; if an anisotropic mineral is arranged so that its optic axis is perpendicular to the thin section, then the mineral will appear dark in all orientations (i.e., it behaves like an isotropic mineral).

Interference colour. You can use the Michel–Levy chart to estimate whether the mineral has high-order or low-order colours. If there are several grains of the same mineral present in the slide, look for the one that shows the highest interference colour.

Twinning. A twinned crystal consists of regions that are very slightly misaligned relative to each other. The different regions of crystal are called twin components and, when viewed between crossed polars, adjacent components will go into extinction in different positions. Simple twins consist of just two components, side by side. However, some minerals (particularly plagioclase feldspar), show multiple twin components and, when viewed between crossed polars, have a banded appearance (rotating the crystal causes the bright and dark bands to swap positions).

3.4.3   GOOD MICROSCOPE PRACTICE

Even using the lowest magnification, your microscope will show only a restricted field of view. Therefore, before you start with the microscope, it's important to get a feel for the overall appearance of a thin section: look at it carefully by holding it up to the light and looking at it with your hand-lens, and note any special textures.

When you put the thin section under the microscope (by placing it on the stage and securing it with the metal stage-clips), you should start by using plane-polarized light, and the lowest possible magnification. Do not turn the brightness up too much, as this can hide certain details of the crystals. Note any differences in relief between different grains. Can you see grain boundaries or cleavage traces? Try to decide, provisionally, how many different minerals are present, then look at several grains of each mineral in turn. Is the mineral coloured? Try rotating the section; is the mineral pleochroic? Does the mineral grain have any particular shape? Does it have a high or low relief?

Between crossed polars, note interference colours, remembering to look for the maximum interference colour for a given mineral type. Is there any relationship between the position in which a mineral becomes extinct, and the directions of any special features (such as twinning or cleavage traces)?

As you 'get your eye in', you can switch back-and-forth between crossed polars and plane-polarized light and, if necessary, switch to higher magnifications. Be sure to re-focus the microscope each time you change the magnification. Take special care if you use the ×40 objective lens, because it is very easy to break the slide if you move the focusing knob too quickly!

Activity 3.7

You should now put these ideas to practical use, by investigating some rocks in thin section, using the polarizing microscope from the Home Kit.

3.5 OBJECTIVES FOR SECTION 3

Now you have completed this Section, you should be able to:

3.1   Suggest different ways in which light passing through a crystalline material is modified.

3.2   Define the term refractive index, and suggest a way of representing its variation with direction in a crystal.

3.3   Explain the meaning of the terms isotropic and anisotropic, and, using examples, suggest factors that might affect the degree of anisotropy of a substance.

3.4   Explain what is meant by double refraction.

3.5   Explain what is meant by the term permitted vibration direction, and suggest how we might determine the permitted vibration directions for a crystal using the optical indicatrix.

3.6   Give an account of the passage of plane-polarized light through an anisotropic crystal on the stage of a polarizing microscope.

3.7   Explain the origin of interference colours in anisotropic materials.

3.8   Define the term birefringence, and suggest a way in which it might be measured.

3.9   Contrast the optical properties of a crystalline and a non-crystalline material.

3.10   Suggest ways in which you might attempt to identify, and distinguish, an unknown mineral (in thin section) using a polarizing microscope.

Now try the following questions to test your understanding of Section 3.

Question 3.2   A slice of an unknown mineral has been examined with a polarizing microscope. In plane-polarized light the mineral appeared colourless, but when viewed between crossed polars it appeared dark, and remained dark as the stage rotated. To what crystal system is this mineral likely to belong?

Question 3.3   In plane-polarized light, a thin section of a mineral shows very high relief, but as the stage is rotated through 90°, this changes to very low relief. Why does the relief change with orientation? What prediction can you make about the interference colour for this mineral?

Question 3.4   In Section 2, you were introduced to the crystal structures of two polymorphs of carbon: diamond and graphite. Based on your knowledge of these structures, what prediction(s) can you make about the optical properties of diamond and graphite?

4 EXPLORING ROCK-FORMING MINERALS

4.1 INTRODUCTION

There are over 100 chemical elements, and one might expect an almost infinite number of different crystalline arrangements to form from them. In fact, the total number of minerals discovered is only about 3500, and the number of commonly occurring *rock-forming* minerals is much smaller. Why such a small number? Although Nature's kitchen has thousands of chemical recipes, most ingredients are in very short supply. Thus the widely occurring, rock-forming minerals represent the combinations of a small number of readily available ingredients, that is, the abundant crustal elements, listed in Table 4.1.

Table 4.1 The average composition of the Earth's crust (only the most abundant elements are listed).

Element	Symbol	% by mass
oxygen	O	46.6
silicon	Si	27.7
aluminium	Al	8.3
iron	Fe	5.0
calcium	Ca	3.6
sodium	Na	2.8
potassium	K	2.6
magnesium	Mg	2.1
others	–	1.3
total		100.0

From Table 4.1, we can see that oxygen and silicon are by far the most abundant elements in the Earth's crust. Minerals containing silicon combined with oxygen are called **silicate minerals**, and are the single most important mineral group – making up over 90% of the Earth's crust.

The non-silicate minerals (of which calcite is perhaps the most familiar example) contain different chemical groups, such as carbon combined with oxygen (**carbonates**) and metals combined with oxygen (**oxides**). Some examples of these different molecular groups are illustrated in Figure 4.1.

Throughout the following Sections you will find descriptions of the crystal structures of important rock-forming minerals. Please note that we don't expect you to remember specific details of structures, merely the essential attributes of, and differences between, structures of the main mineral groups. Activity 4.8 gives you the opportunity to visualize many aspects of these structures using an interactive multimedia package on DVD 1, and you may wish to start looking at the multimedia mineral models as you work through Section 4, instead of waiting until the very end.

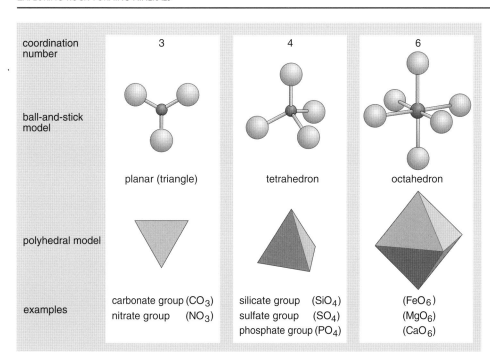

coordination number	3	4	6
ball-and-stick model			
	planar (triangle)	tetrahedron	octahedron
polyhedral model			
examples	carbonate group (CO$_3$) nitrate group (NO$_3$)	silicate group (SiO$_4$) sulfate group (SO$_4$) phosphate group (PO$_4$)	(FeO$_6$) (MgO$_6$) (CaO$_6$)

Figure 4.1   Molecular groups found in common rock-forming minerals. In each of these cases, the coordination number is the number of oxygen atoms that are nearest neighbours to the central atom of the group.

4.2 THE SILICATE BUILDING GAME

Silicate minerals all share the same basic building block: a silicon atom bonded to four oxygen atoms at the corners of a tetrahedron, called the **silicate group** (or SiO$_4$ group: Figure 4.1). We shall treat the Si–O bond as being essentially covalent in nature; however, when trying to balance mineral formulae it is often convenient to imagine that Si and O are electrically charged, giving an (SiO$_4$)$^{4-}$ unit. It is also important to bear in mind that silicate structures may contain other kinds of atom (e.g., Na or K), whose bonding (e.g., to oxygen) tends to have a more ionic nature.

The wide range of silicate structures reflects different ways of connecting the SiO$_4$ groups to build three-dimensional structures, and the range of other atoms that can be squeezed into the structures. For example, one type of structure (the mineral **olivine**) has isolated SiO$_4$ groups interspersed with metal atoms (which bind the silicate groups together) – whereas many other silicate structures contain SiO$_4$ groups which are directly linked together. In fact, the connectivity of SiO$_4$ groups provides a way of grouping these otherwise diverse minerals into a small number of structural categories.

During cooling of melts rich in SiO$_2$ there is a tendency for SiO$_4$ groups to join together, or polymerize, forming almost infinite chains of interlinked groups: oxygen atoms become shared between two silicon atoms (Figure 4.2).

❑   With reference to Figure 4.2, how would you determine the ratio of silicon atoms to oxygen atoms in an infinite chain of silicate tetrahedra?

■   The ratio of silicon to oxygen atoms is affected by the number of Si–O–Si linkages. Each silicon is bonded to four oxygen atoms, and we need to consider which of these are shared by other silicon atoms. Figure 4.2 shows that two of the four oxygen atoms aren't bonded to other silicon atoms; the remaining two oxygen atoms are each shared with another silicon atom. Thus, for every silicon atom, there are $2 + \frac{1}{2} + \frac{1}{2} = 3$ oxygen atoms, giving a Si:O ratio of 1:3.

These **chain structures** are characteristic of **pyroxene** minerals, and because of the corner-sharing of oxygen atoms, the ratio of silicon to oxygen has increased from 1:4 (structures with isolated SiO$_4$ groups) to 1:3 (infinite chains).

Figure 4.2 Polymerization of SiO$_4$ groups, to make an infinite silicate chain, n(SiO$_3$).

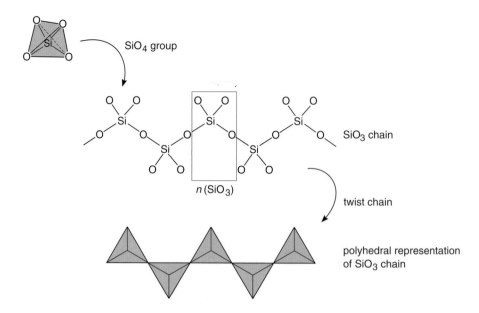

Polymerization doesn't necessarily stop at single chains. Pairs of silicate chains may join together, to give double chains, e.g., **amphibole** minerals (Figure 4.3). Here, the silicon-to-oxygen ratio has increased from 1:3 to 1:2.75 (i.e., 4:11). If we were to keep joining chains together, we'd end up with an infinite sheet (Si:O ratio = 1:2.5). A fully polymerized structure would have every oxygen atom acting as a bridge between two silicon atoms, giving a Si:O ratio of 1:2 (which is the ratio for quartz, which has a three-dimensional framework structure).

Other arrangements of silicate tetrahedra are also possible, including 'bow-ties' (pairs of corner-linked tetrahedra) and rings (e.g., six-fold rings of tetrahedra in the mineral cordierite). However, these arrangements are much rarer than those illustrated in Figure 4.3.

The real world turns out to be just a little more complex than our simple picture makes out. We've only considered silicon atoms at the centre of the tetrahedra, but some structures contain AlO$_4$ groups, where an aluminium atom has replaced a silicon atom. Our Si:O ratios should therefore be interpreted as the ratio of the number of tetrahedral sites to the number of oxygen atoms (i.e., T:O). Thus, increasing polymerization results in more oxygen atoms being shared between tetrahedral sites, and consequently an increase in the T:O ratio.

We have seen that just by manipulating a basic structural unit, the silicate tetrahedron, we can generate a number of different 'template' structures. It is important to realize that these templates define the positions of all the oxygen atoms in the structure (i.e., at the corners of the tetrahedra), plus the tetrahedral atoms (generally silicon and/or aluminium). The templates are not complete, however, because we require other, positively charged atoms, to compensate for any excess negative charge on the silicate groups. These ions, usually metals, reside in cavities or interstices generated by the tetrahedral structure, and they help to bind the three-dimensional structure together.

The following Sections introduce you to some of the important rock-forming minerals, with practical Activities using your Home Kit (hand specimens and microscope work). You will probably find it most convenient to set up your Home Kit before you start these Sections, so that you can work your way through the various Activities as you study the text.

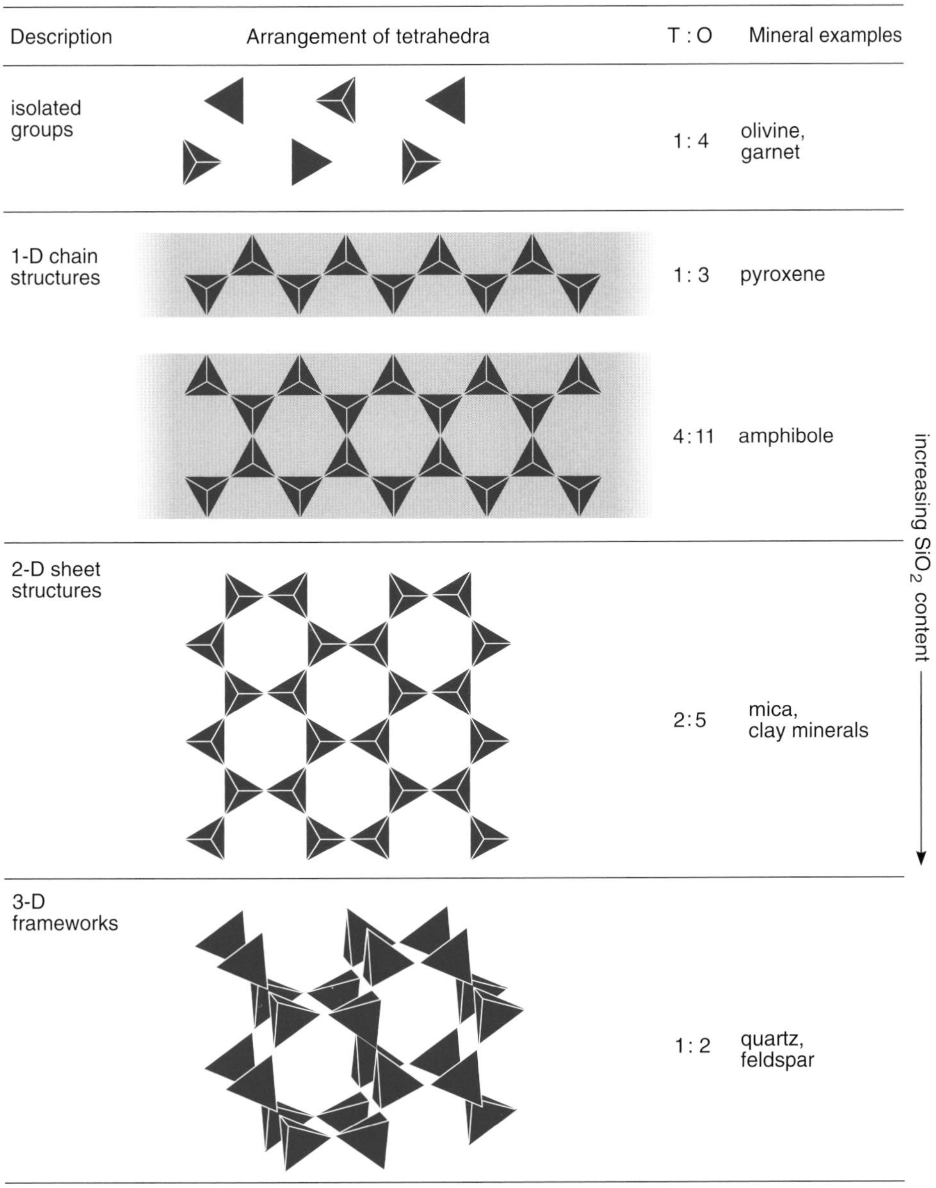

Description	Arrangement of tetrahedra	T : O	Mineral examples
isolated groups		1 : 4	olivine, garnet
1-D chain structures		1 : 3	pyroxene
		4 : 11	amphibole
2-D sheet structures		2 : 5	mica, clay minerals
3-D frameworks		1 : 2	quartz, feldspar

increasing SiO$_2$ content →

Figure 4.3 Structural classification of some common silicate minerals, based on the polymerization of the silicate tetrahedra. The structures shown are only very small parts of what are effectively infinite structures. The ratio of the tetrahedral (T) sites to oxygen (O) sites is given for each structure. Increasing polymerization results in proportionally more oxygen atoms being shared between tetrahedral sites, and consequently an increase in the T : O ratio.

4.3 MINERALS WITH ISOLATED SiO$_4$ TETRAHEDRA

Isolated tetrahedral silicates are the simplest structures in the silicate hierarchy. They also have the lowest Si : O ratio (1 : 4), and are therefore likely to be formed from silica-poor melts.

4.3.1 OLIVINE

The mineral olivine is probably the most important example of a structure with isolated tetrahedra. Every SiO$_4$ group has a net charge of -4, and to balance this out (the crystal has to be electrically neutral!) olivine contains two doubly charged (divalent) positive ions per SiO$_4$ unit. The name 'olivine' actually refers to a continuous spread of chemical compositions between Mg$_2$SiO$_4$ and Fe$_2$SiO$_4$, and we usually write its formula as (Mg,Fe)$_2$SiO$_4$, indicating that magnesium and iron can substitute for each other. This kind of chemical mixing is called a **solid solution** and occurs when two atoms have similar *sizes* and *charges* (e.g., Mg^{2+} and Fe^{2+}), so that either atom could fit into the same interstitial site in a crystal structure.

Where do the metal ions go? Earlier, we said that the oxygen atoms in the silicate groups provide a structural template for the metal and silicon atoms. In olivine, the oxygen atoms form close-packed layers, which are very similar to the hexagonal close-packed (i.e., ABAB) arrangement that we examined in Section 2. (An important difference, however, is that, unlike the atoms in a metal, the oxygen atoms in olivine don't actually touch – instead, they repel each other slightly.)

❑   If a structure has an hexagonal close-packed arrangement of oxygen atoms, where will any other atoms fit in?

■   We've seen that hexagonal close-packed structures contain two kinds of *interstice*: tetrahedral interstices (between four oxygen atoms, Figure 2.15a), and octahedral interstices (between six oxygen atoms, Figure 2.15b).

The close-packed oxygen arrangement provides both types of interstitial site: silicon atoms reside in tetrahedral interstices – i.e., at the centres of SiO_4 tetrahedra; the remaining, octahedral, interstices, contain the larger magnesium and iron atoms (Figure 4.4). Compared with other silicates, olivine therefore has a relatively high density.

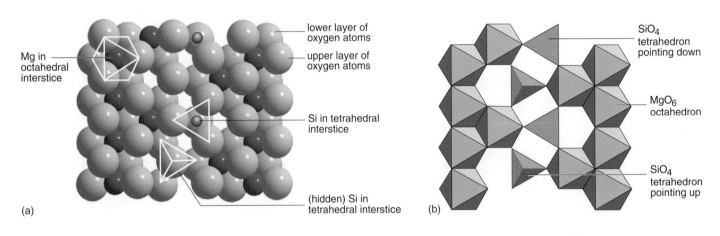

(a)
Mg in octahedral interstice

lower layer of oxygen atoms
upper layer of oxygen atoms

Si in tetrahedral interstice

(hidden) Si in tetrahedral interstice

(b)
SiO_4 tetrahedron pointing down

MgO_6 octahedron

SiO_4 tetrahedron pointing up

Figure 4.4   The olivine structure. (a) A space-filling model, showing two layers of virtually close-packed oxygen atoms, with Mg and Si filling some (but not all) of the interstices between the layers. (b) A polyhedral model of this arrangement, showing the isolated SiO_4 groups in blue, and the edge-linked MgO_6 octahedra.

The strong three-dimensional bonding pattern also means that olivine is a hard mineral, without any good cleavage. When there is lots of iron present olivine has a characteristic olive-green colour.

Olivine crystallizes at very high temperatures from melts that are rich in metals (e.g., iron and magnesium) and relatively poor in silica (SiO_2). Because olivine is one of the first phases to crystallize as a melt cools, it is often found as well-formed crystals, surrounded by later-crystallizing minerals (which tend to be smaller, and lack such ideal crystal shapes).

At ambient temperatures and pressures, olivine is not very stable and is liable to break down or alter, to oxide minerals. Under the microscope, olivine crystals show evidence of this alteration in the form of curved, irregular cracks filled with iron oxide and other new minerals.

Activity 4.1

This short Activity introduces you to olivine in hand specimen and thin section.

4.3.2 OLIVINE/SPINEL PHASE TRANSITION

We've seen that the olivine structure can be described in terms of a hexagonal close-packed arrangement of oxygen atoms, with Mg, Fe and Si filling interstices in the structure. Silicate **spinel** is the cubic close-packed equivalent of olivine: it has the same chemical formula, but the stacking of the (almost) close-packed oxygen layers follows an ABCABC pattern, rather than the ABABAB pattern of olivine.

Silicate spinel is slightly denser than olivine, and is more stable at higher pressures. Because olivine and silicate spinel have the same chemical composition, and because their structures have similar arrangements of oxygen atoms, it is possible to convert one into the other, by applying pressure. The resulting phase transition involves the shearing of oxygen layers, and the rearrangement of magnesium and iron atoms between the layers. This requires the breaking of chemical bonds and some diffusion of ions – and is termed a **reconstructive phase transition**.

❑ Can you think of any geological situations where olivine might be subjected to very high pressures?

■ Olivine is a major constituent of the rock basalt, which erupts at mid-ocean ridges, and makes up most of the oceanic crust. If the oceanic crust is subducted into the mantle, then the olivine will be subjected to very high pressures.

Conversion from olivine into spinel is indeed believed to occur as oceanic crust is subducted deep into the mantle (you will come across this in Block 3). Because of the density difference between the two phases, the olivine/spinel phase transition results in a reduction in volume. In a cold, subducting slab of oceanic crust, this reconstructive phase transition is delayed until the slab has been subducted further and heated by the surrounding mantle. When the phase transition does finally occur, the sudden volume reduction triggers seismic waves, which may cause earthquakes.

4.3.3 GARNET

Garnet is another dense mineral. Its crystal structure is rather complex, but it is related to that of spinel, though with a much larger unit cell. Essentially, the structure contains quasi-close-packed layers of oxygen atoms, with silicon and other atoms in interstices between the layers. At the very high pressures in the Earth's mantle, silicate spinel transforms to garnet. Unlike olivine, garnet belongs to the cubic system. It is also something of a 'chemical dustbin', and a vast range of chemical compositions is possible. Garnet can contain aluminium, calcium, iron, magnesium and many rare-earth elements, such as yttrium (some lasers contain crystals of synthetic yttrium aluminium garnet).

Activity 4.2

This short Activity introduces you to garnet in hand specimen and thin section.

4.4 CHAIN SILICATES

4.4.1 PYROXENES

Pyroxene minerals are examples of polymerized silicates, with chains of SiO_4 tetrahedra, similar to the one depicted in Figure 4.2. In the full three-dimensional structure of pyroxene, chains are interconnected via strong bonds to one set of metal atoms, called the B sites. Each B-site metal atom (often Mg or Fe) is surrounded by six oxygen atoms, at the corners of an octahedron. Thus, a chain sandwich is formed, with tetrahedral chains at the top and bottom, and an octahedral chain in the middle. Seen end-on, this chain-sandwich resembles a capital letter I, and is referred to as an I-beam. It is a strong, cohesive element in the structure (Figure 4.5b).

Adjacent I-beams mesh into each other, and are weakly bonded by a second set of metal atoms, residing in A sites (the A sites are larger than the B sites, and can contain larger atoms, such as Ca). For every two SiO_3 chain units, there is one A site and one B site. The general formula of a pyroxene is usually written $ABSi_2O_6$ (where A and B refer to divalent metal ions in the A and B sites, respectively). Important pyroxenes include clinopyroxene ($Ca(Mg,Fe)Si_2O_6$) and orthopyroxene ($(Mg,Fe)_2Si_2O_6$).

❏ Which metal atoms go into which sites for clinopyroxene?

■ Using the general formula $ABSi_2O_6$, Ca goes into the A site, and the B site contains a mixture of Mg and Fe atoms. Note that the formula of clinopyroxene implies that there is a solid solution, from $CaMgSi_2O_6$ to $CaFeSi_2O_6$.

The differences between the A and B sites are important, because this is the key to understanding the mechanical properties of pyroxene. The pyroxene structure is not uniformly strong: the regions between the I-beams are relatively weak areas, and if the structure is stressed, it is likely to break – or cleave – along these directions. This gives two good cleavage directions, at approximately 90° to each other (Figure 4.5c).

Figure 4.5 Structure and cleavage in pyroxene. (a) A single chain of SiO_4 tetrahedra, and its end-on appearance. (b) Part of the pyroxene crystal structure, viewed along the chain direction, showing arrangement of the A (white) and B (black) sites between the chains. (c) Cleavage directions do not cut through the strong I-beam units, but break the bonds to the A sites. Two sets of cleavages may be observed, at approximately 90° to each other.

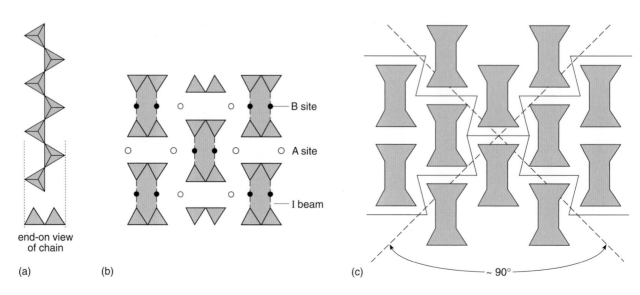

❏ When you are observing cleavage in thin section, will the traces always be at 90° to each other?

■ You will see two sets of cleavage traces at 90° to each other only if you're looking exactly parallel to the chain direction. If you were looking perpendicular to this direction, you would only see one set of cleavage traces. This is illustrated in Figure 4.6a.

4.4.2 AMPHIBOLES

Amphibole minerals contain double silicate chains, with the formula $n(Si_4O_{11})$ (Figure 4.3). This arrangement of the double chains resembles the pyroxene structure, with strong I-beam units, giving two distinct cleavages. However, because the chains are wider than the pyroxene single chains, the cleavage angle is increased from 90° to 120°. This is illustrated in Figure 4.6b.

Amphibole is found in many metamorphic rocks, and usually contains **hydroxyl (OH) groups** (a hydrogen atom bonded to an oxygen atom). The general formula of amphibole can be written $AB_2C_5Si_8O_{22}(OH)_2$ (where A represents a large metal atom such as Na, and B and C represent smaller metal atoms, such as Ca or Mg).

Amphibole can be distinguished from pyroxene in thin section because of its 120° (or 60°) cleavage (Figure 4.6), and because some common varieties of amphibole are strongly pleochroic (showing yellow–green–brown colours).

> ## Activity 4.3
>
> You should now complete Activity 4.3, in which you will examine both amphibole and pyroxene in thin section.

4.5 SHEET SILICATES

The sheet silicates form a large number of different minerals, including mica, but they all share the same basic building blocks: a tetrahedral sheet, and one of two kinds of octahedral sheet. The sheets are combined to form composite structures, e.g., an octahedral sheet sandwiched between two tetrahedral sheets (Figure 4.7).

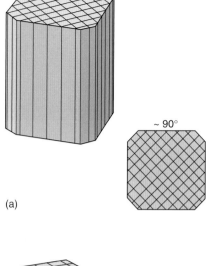

(a)

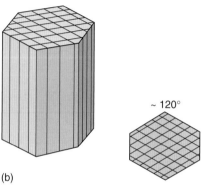

(b)

Figure 4.6 Sketches of single crystals showing cleavage traces for (a) pyroxene and (b) amphibole.

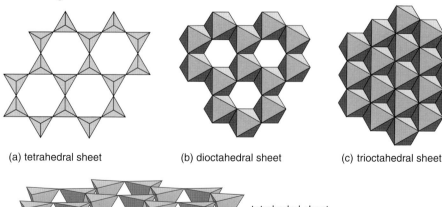

(a) tetrahedral sheet (b) dioctahedral sheet (c) trioctahedral sheet

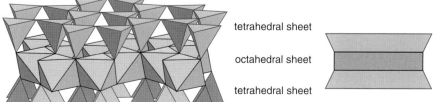

(d) sheet sandwich

tetrahedral sheet
octahedral sheet
tetrahedral sheet

(e) schematic representation

Figure 4.7 Building blocks of sheet silicate minerals. (a) Part of a tetrahedral sheet. (b) Part of an $Al(OH)_3$ octahedral sheet. Every oxygen atom is shared between two octahedra, so this is called a *di*-octahedral sheet. (c) Part of an $Mg(OH)_2$ octahedral sheet. Every oxygen atom is shared between three octahedra, so this is called a *tri*-octahedral sheet. (d) An oblique view of a sheet sandwich, formed by two tetrahedral sheets bonded to an octahedral sheet. (e) A schematic representation of a sheet sandwich.

The octahedral sheets could be thought of as layers of metal hydroxides (e.g., a trioctahedral sheet is equivalent to a layer of magnesium hydroxide, $Mg(OH)_2$). Each magnesium is bonded to six OH groups, at the corners of an octahedron. The octahedra are arranged in a plane, sharing edges; each oxygen atom is shared between *three* octahedra.

The other kind of octahedral sheet contains aluminium instead of magnesium, and is equivalent to a layer of aluminium hydroxide, $Al(OH)_3$. Because the valency of aluminium (3) is greater than that of magnesium (2), the $Al(OH)_3$ sheet contains holes. Each oxygen atom is shared between *two* octahedra, hence this is called a dioctahedral sheet.

A common feature of all sheet silicate minerals is that they tend to be soft, with near-perfect cleavage parallel to the sheets, and so they form distinctive, platy or flake-like crystals. We shall investigate these properties in more detail in the next Section.

4.5.1 THE MICA GROUP

Mica is a general name given to a range of minerals that have sandwich structures weakly bonded by interlayer ions, such as potassium. Each sandwich contains two tetrahedral sheets on either side of an octahedral sheet (Figure 4.7d). One in four of the tetrahedra contains Al instead of Si (though the number of oxygen atoms remains unchanged), with the result that sheets have an excess negative charge. This is balanced by the presence of interlayer positive ions.

Whereas the bonding inside a sandwich is very strong, the bonding between the sandwiches (provided by the interlayer ions) is very weak and it is possible to slide one sandwich past another one. Thus, mica has perfect cleavage, and it is easy to split a mica crystal into thin, transparent flakes (such as the thin flakes, MS II, in your Home Kit).

We've seen that there are two possibilities for making the octahedral layers: either an $Al(OH)_3$ layer (dioctahedral), or an $Mg(OH)_2$ layer (trioctahedral). These give rise to two important mica minerals: **muscovite** (white mica) is the Al-rich form, and biotite (brown mica) is the Mg-rich form. Note that, in biotite, some Mg is replaced by Fe.

❏ Why should biotite be brown and muscovite be white?
■ We've already seen that minerals containing large amounts of Fe tend to have dark colours, and this is also true of biotite. Muscovite does not contain any Fe, and so is light coloured.

The structures of muscovite and biotite are given, in schematic form, in Figure 4.8.

4.5.2 CLAY MINERALS

Clay minerals are related to the muscovite structure, but there is no aluminium in the tetrahedral layers (any aluminium in the structure is restricted to $Al(OH)_3$ dioctahedral layers). Clay minerals tend to occur in large masses of fine-grained, platy particles, in clay. Many clay minerals (such as smectite, in Figure 4.8) allow water molecules to reside between their sandwich layers, and this gives clay its plastic properties as the sandwich units slide over each other.

These minerals are stable at low temperatures and in the presence of water, and tend to form from the chemical breakdown of high-temperature K/Al silicate minerals, such as K-feldspar ($KAlSi_3O_8$). The china clay found in Cornwall is derived from the decomposition of feldspar in granite.

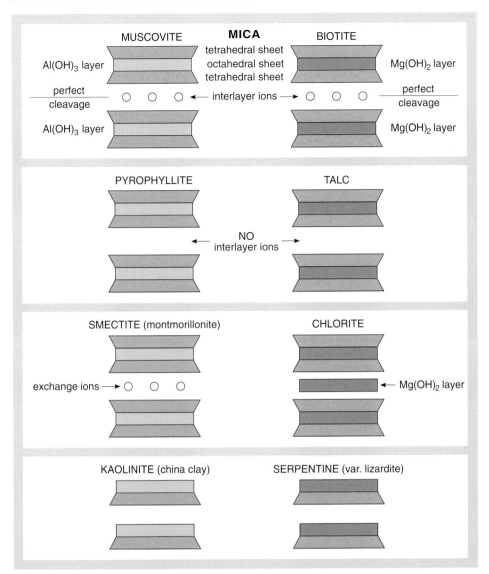

Figure 4.8   Structural relationships between sheet silicate minerals, in terms of the stacking of tetrahedral and octahedral layers. On the left are shown minerals related to muscovite (Al-rich); on the right are shown minerals related to biotite (Mg-rich).

The large gaps between the sheets, and the large surface areas of the sheets, mean that clay minerals readily adsorb ions and molecules. This makes them very useful as ion-exchange agents, for purification purposes, and as catalysts to speed up chemical reactions (e.g., smectite in Figure 4.8).

4.5.3   OTHER SHEET SILICATES

Some important non-mica, non-clay sheet silicates you are likely to meet include talc, chlorite and serpentine – all of which have structures related to biotite (summarized in the right-hand column of Figure 4.8). Unlike biotite, however, their tetrahedral layers contain no aluminium, only silicon. The layers therefore have no net electrical charge, and so no interlayer ions are required. Without the interlayer ions, there is virtually nothing to hold the sandwiches together. (There is an extremely weak electrostatic attraction, caused by variations in the electron distribution within the sandwiches, resulting in the possibility of positively charged regions of one sandwich attracting negatively charged regions in another sandwich.)

❑   How do the hardness of talc and serpentine compare with the hardness of biotite?

■   Without interlayer ions between the sheet sandwiches, these minerals become extremely soft. Talc is one of the softest minerals known, with a hardness equal to 1 on Mohs' scale (Table 2.2).

These minerals are stable at low temperatures and in the presence of water, and tend to form from the breakdown of high-temperature Mg-rich minerals – particularly olivine (Mg_2SiO_4).

Activity 4.4

You should now complete Activity 4.4, in which you will investigate two sheet silicate minerals, biotite and muscovite, in hand specimen and thin section.

4.6 FRAMEWORK SILICATES

The framework silicates are the most abundant silicates in the Earth's crust. They have complex crystal structures, with each SiO_4 tetrahedron joined to four others, giving a fully polymerized, three-dimensional framework. If some of the silicon atoms are replaced by aluminium, then other metal atoms (e.g., sodium or potassium) are required to maintain charge balance. These 'extra' atoms reside in cavities in the aluminosilicate framework.

4.6.1 SILICA MINERALS

The **silica minerals** have fully polymerized structures and are chemically very pure SiO_2. At the Earth's surface, the most stable structure for the composition SiO_2 is the **quartz** structure, which is illustrated in Figure 4.9.

❑ Can you correlate the directions of the helices in quartz with the single crystal of quartz (MS VII) in the Home Kit?

■ Looking down the helix axis, we see six-fold symmetry. This corresponds to looking down the long axis of your quartz crystal. It is important to note that, although the prism faces in the quartz crystal may be of different sizes, the interfacial angles are all exactly 60° (Figure 4.10).

Figure 4.9 Idealized crystal structure of quartz, SiO_2. (a) SiO_4 tetrahedra are arranged in helices, spiralling around like a 'barber's pole' (top). Looking along the helix axis, this gives the appearance of a hexagonal ring (bottom). (b) The full three-dimensional structure contains interlinked six-fold and three-fold helices. The dashed lines indicate the edges of one unit cell.

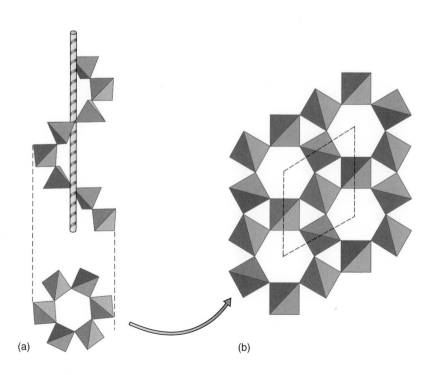

(a)   (b)

The strong, three-dimensional bonding in quartz, with no definite planes of weakness, means that it does not show cleavage, but when subjected to extreme force will shatter into curved, glassy fragments. The strong bonding also makes quartz very hard, and extremely resistant to chemical attack. This means that quartz grains can survive transport by rivers or by wind over vast distances, eventually being deposited as sand grains.

Although quartz is very pure SiO_2, it can sometimes contain small amounts of impurities such as aluminium, iron, lithium and titanium. The effect of these impurities is totally out of proportion to their minute concentrations, as they cause quite dramatic colours in what would otherwise be an entirely colourless mineral. Plate 4.1 shows some coloured varieties of quartz.

Despite the apparent durability of quartz, it is stable over only a limited range of pressures and temperatures. Our idealized quartz structure exists only at high temperatures. The form of quartz seen at room temperature is a slightly distorted variety called α-quartz (alpha-quartz), in which the six-fold symmetrical rings are distorted and show only three-fold symmetry. If α-quartz is heated, the tetrahedra twist to their symmetrical positions; at temperatures above 573 °C, the idealized, hexagonal structure is attained. This is called β-quartz (beta-quartz). This kind of atomic rearrangement, which does not require the breaking of any chemical bonds, is called a **displacive phase transition**, and proceeds very quickly.

Displacive phase transitions turn out to be very common in framework silicate minerals. Most involve twisting of SiO_4 tetrahedra relative to each other: the shared oxygen atom between two tetrahedra acts as a 'universal joint', and the complete structure is actually rather floppy. Displacive phase transitions are important because they account for significant energy changes in the crystal – and this will dramatically affect the stability of one mineral compared with other possible forms.

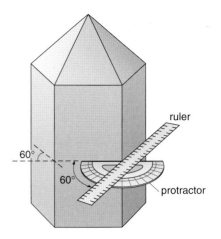

Figure 4.10 Idealized quartz crystal, showing that the prism faces are 60° apart.

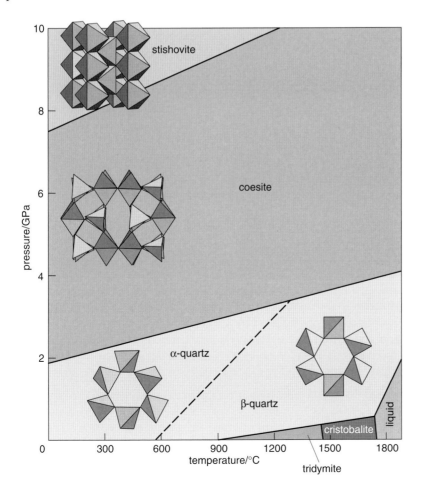

Figure 4.11   Phase diagram for SiO_2. (The unit of pressure is gigapascals, abbreviated as GPa, where $1\,\text{GPa} = 10^9\,\text{Pa} = 10^9\,\text{N m}^{-2}$.)

A phase diagram for silica is shown in Figure 4.11. It shows more information than the H_2O phase diagram that you met earlier (Figure 2.2) because it distinguishes several different *solid* phases. Thus, the quartz structure is only one of several different solid phases that have the same composition. These phases are polymorphs of SiO_2.

The different phases have very different crystal structures, so to convert one phase (e.g., quartz) into another (e.g., tridymite) would require breaking up one structure, and growing the new phase from scratch: a reconstructive phase transition (such as you met in Section 4.2.2 with olivine and spinel). Whereas displacive phase transitions (e.g., α-quartz → β-quartz) are very fast, requiring very little energy, a reconstructive phase transition (e.g., quartz → tridymite) is very slow – and may not occur at all if a high-temperature phase such as tridymite or cristobalite is cooled very rapidly (quenched) to room temperature. When such a phase exists well outside its stability field, the phase is said to be **metastable**.

❑   Can you think of any other phases that are preserved outside their stability fields?

■   In Section 2.3.3, we looked at two polymorphs of carbon: diamond and graphite. Diamond is a high-pressure polymorph of carbon; at the Earth's surface it is less stable than another carbon polymorph, graphite. However, there is a huge energy barrier required to break down the diamond structure, so diamond can persist *metastably* at the Earth's surface.

Stishovite is a very high pressure form of silica in which each silicon atom is bonded to *six* oxygen atoms, at the corners of an octahedron. Stishovite has been found in meteorite impact craters in the desert, where desert sand (quartz) has been subjected to very high pressures and temperatures, and forced to undergo a reconstructive phase transition. Stishovite may also exist deep in the Earth's interior.

Question 4.1   What pressure would be required to convert silica into stishovite at 300 °C?

Activity 4.5

At the beginning of this Block, we showed a photograph of a gem-quality quartz crystal, with a well-defined hexagonal appearance. Although quartz is a very common mineral, it is more usually found in the form of mineral grains, inside rocks. In this Activity, you will look at quartz grains in a rock hand specimen, and examine their optical properties.

4.6.2   FELDSPARS

Feldspar makes up approximately 70% of the Earth's crust, yet is one of the most complex and poorly understood of all minerals. The name feldspar actually refers to a *group* of silicate minerals, which share the same basic structure: some silicon replaced by aluminium, with K, Na or Ca ions inside cavities of the tetrahedral framework. The three most important feldspar species are: **orthoclase** (K[AlSi$_3$]O$_8$), **albite** (Na[AlSi$_3$]O$_8$), and **anorthite** (Ca[Al$_2$Si$_2$]O$_8$) (the elements listed in square brackets occupy the tetrahedral sites).

At very high temperatures there is complete solid solution between orthoclase and albite, i.e., K and Na substitute for each other (in the same way that Fe and Mg substitute for each other in olivine). Feldspars with compositions within this range are called **alkali feldspars**. At lower temperatures the alkali feldspar solid solution is less stable, and if an alkali feldspar crystal of intermediate

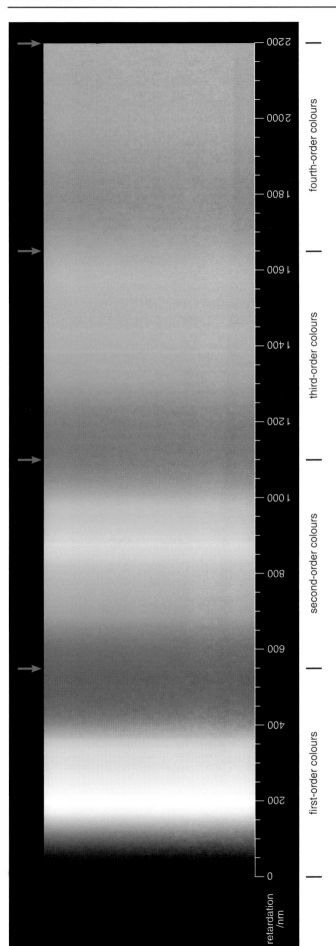

retardation /nm

Plate 3.1 The Michel–Levy chart. The scale of interference colours on a quartz wedge. The colours are divided into different orders, separated by the bright pink bands, and indicated by the red arrows.

(Please note: the first-order yellow/orange may show a slight greenish tint due to the limitations of colour printing.)

Plate 4.1 Crystals of the mineral quartz showing a range of coloration, caused by slight variations in chemical composition. Pure quartz (SiO_2) is colourless; minute amounts of iron (about 50 ppm) induce a purple coloration, characteristic of the quartz variety popularly known as amethyst. Trace amounts of titanium (about 4 ppm) present with iron cause yellow (citrine) or pink (rose quartz) colours. Small amounts of aluminium in otherwise pure quartz may cause a dark coloration (smoky quartz). The largest specimen is 7 cm across.

Plate 6.1 Vertical columnar joints in a basalt lava flow, Giant's Causeway, Northern Ireland.

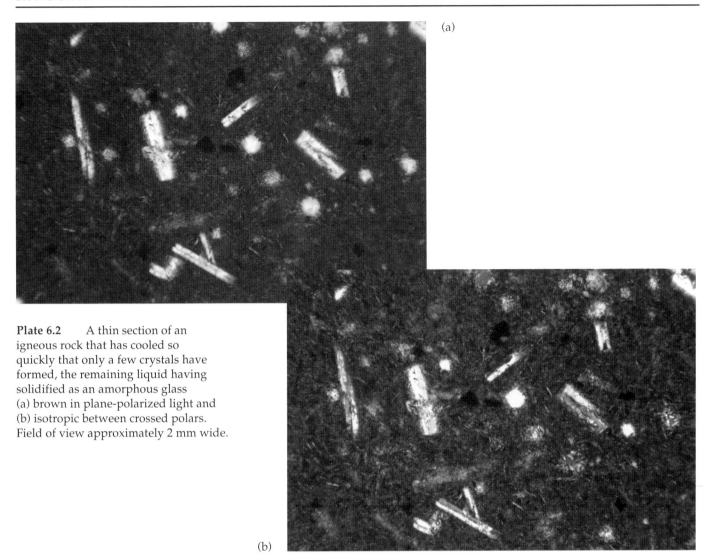

(a)

(b)

Plate 6.2 A thin section of an igneous rock that has cooled so quickly that only a few crystals have formed, the remaining liquid having solidified as an amorphous glass (a) brown in plane-polarized light and (b) isotropic between crossed polars. Field of view approximately 2 mm wide.

Plate 6.3 The natural glass obsidian, which forms when a silica-rich lava cools too quickly for crystals to form. Note the characteristic black, shiny appearance (due to iron impurities) and curved fracture surfaces.

Plate 6.4   A thin section of a rock similar to thin section (TS) G from the Home Kit, viewed under the microscope between crossed polars, using the ×10 objective. Field of view approximately 3 mm wide.

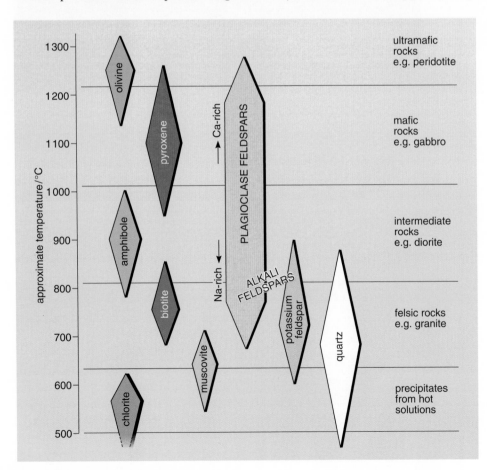

Plate 6.5   Ranges of crystallization temperatures for common minerals of igneous rocks and the mineral associations of peridotite, gabbro, diorite and granite.

Plate 6.6   A basaltic sill concordantly intruding layered sedimentary rocks:
Beacon Valley, Transantarctic Mountains, Antarctica.

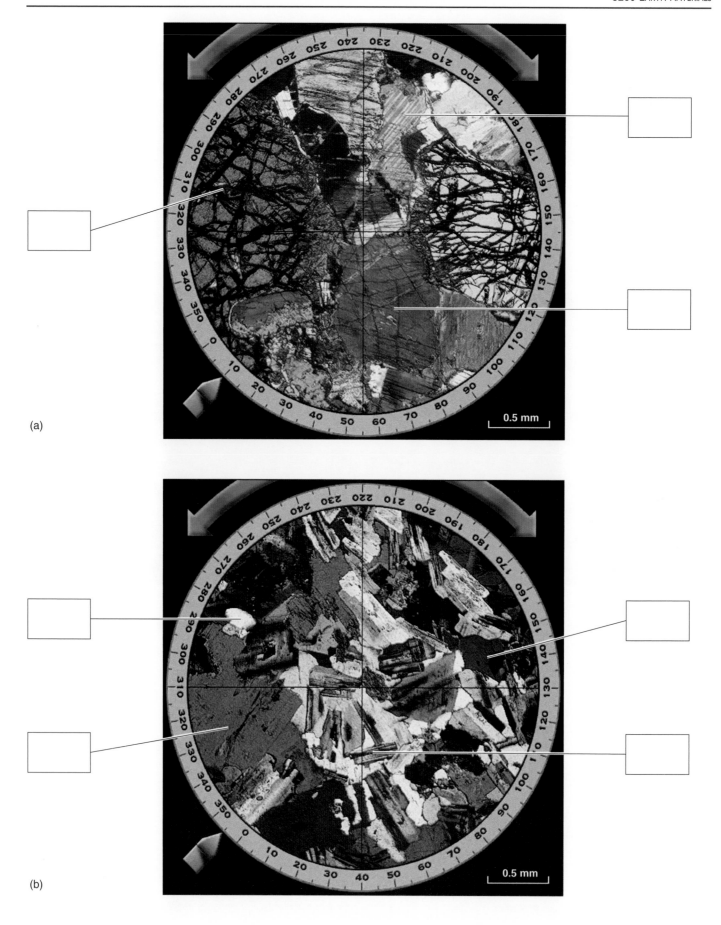

(a)

(b)

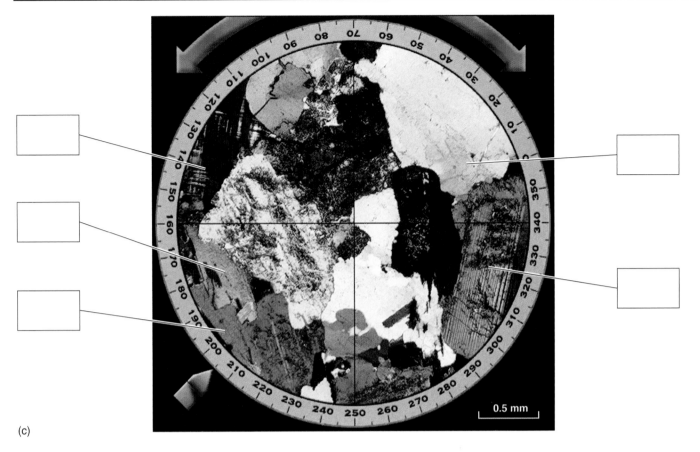

(c)

Plate 6.7 'Digital Microscope' images of thin sections (between crossed polars) of (a) RS 19 (TS K), (b) RS 9 (TS D) and (c) RS 13 (TS E). Blank labels should be filled in at the end of Activity 6.4.

(a)

Plate 6.8 (a) A lava flow, Hawaii; (b) a pyroclastic eruption, Montserrat.

(b)

Plate 6.9   A pegmatite vein, containing large crystals of grey-white quartz and pink potassium (orthoclase) feldspar, from the margin of the Ballater granite, Scotland.

Plate 6.10   An aplite vein (folded) cutting dark, banded metamorphic rocks and a sheet-like microgranite intrusion, Cordillera Darwin, Tierra del Fuego, Chile.

Plate 6.11   A vein of blue-grey molybdenite (MoS_2), an ore of molybdenum, in porphyritic granite, Shap, Cumbria.

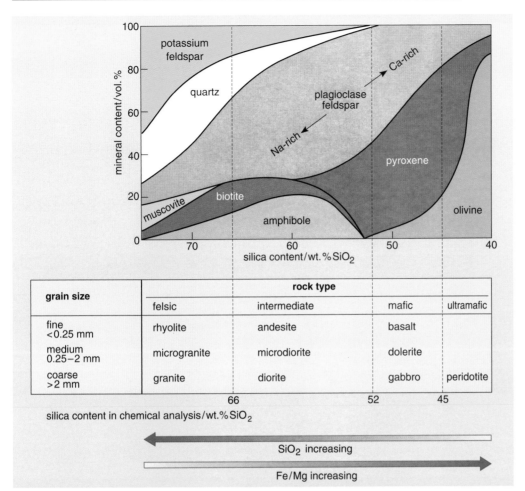

Plate 6.12 A diagram showing the approximate mineral and silica contents of different igneous rocks. Mafic minerals are olivine, pyroxene, amphibole and biotite; felsic minerals are quartz, feldspar and muscovite.

Plate 7.1 Bedded sedimentary rocks exposed in a cliff-face, Argentina. Here hard, prominent beds of limestone are more resistant to weathering than the softer intervening mudstone layers which are cut back.

Plate 7.2 Examples of evaporite minerals: (a) halite, showing cubic crystal shape (actual size) and (b) gypsum, showing two different forms (i) 'swallow-tail' twins (ii) fibrous 'satin spar' (actual size).

(a)

(bi)

(bii)

Plate 7.3   Chert (flint) nodule in chalk showing conchoidal fracture surfaces.

Plate 8.1   Spotted slate from the contact metamorphic zone surrounding the Skiddaw granite intrusion, Lake District. The 'spots' are due to the growth of the mineral andalusite within the country rock as it was metamorphosed by the heat of the intruding granite. Field of view approximately 8 cm wide.

Plate 8.2 Migmatite, showing patchy domains of felsic and mafic minerals.

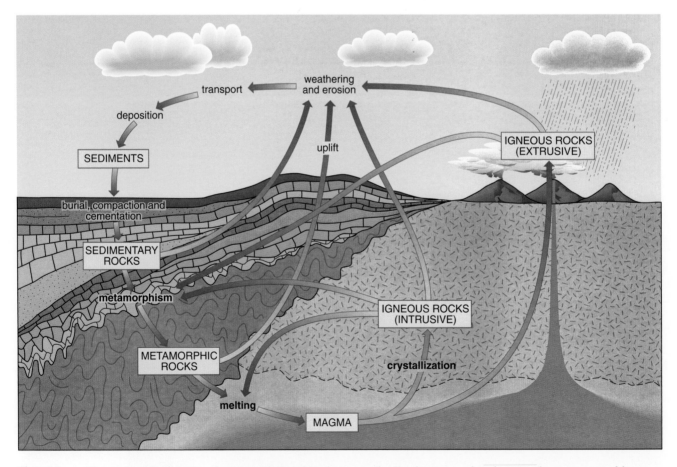

Plate 9.1 The rock cycle showing the inter-relationships between the Earth's internal and external processes and how each of the three major rock groups is related to the others.

composition (e.g., $Na_{0.5}K_{0.5}AlSi_3O_8$) is cooled very slowly, it may 'unmix' into Na-rich and K-rich phases – a process known as exsolution ('from solution'). The result is a usually a mineral grain of one composition (e.g., Na-rich), containing streaks of another composition (e.g., K-rich), giving what is known as **perthitic texture** (particularly noticeable when the grain is viewed in thin section, between crossed polars). You will see an example of perthitic texture in Activity 6.2.

There is also complete solid solution between albite and anorthite at high temperatures, and these are referred to as **plagioclase feldspars**. Solid solution in plagioclase feldspars is rather more complex because some of the substituting ions (Na and Ca) have different charges. A **coupled substitution** is required to maintain charge balance; that is, two substitutions occur simultaneously:

Na⁺ substitutes for Ca^{2+} *and* Si^{4+} substitutes for Al^{3+}

This coupled substitution is more usually written as:

$$Na^+ + Si^{4+} \Leftrightarrow Ca^{2+} + Al^{3+}$$

The overall compositional range of feldspars is plotted as a **ternary diagram** shown in Figure 4.12. Ternary diagrams are very useful devices in geology, which you will meet several times later in the course. Their use is explained in Box 4.1.

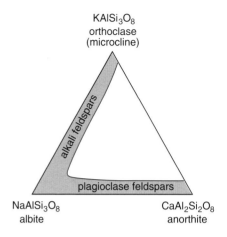

Figure 4.12 A ternary diagram showing the extent of solid solution in alkali and plagioclase feldspars at high temperatures.

Box 4.1 Ternary diagrams

A ternary diagram can be used to plot the composition of a mineral (or indeed, any substance or mixture) in terms of three end-member components (A, B and C). The diagram consists of a triangle, with corners representing the three end members (100% A, 100% B, 100% C). To plot a composition, we need to indicate the proportion of each of the three components. For example, Figure 4.13a shows a system with three components A, B, and C and with different proportions of component A represented by lines parallel to the edge BC.

Suppose we have a mineral whose composition is: 40% A, 30% B and 30% C. We first determine on which 'A' line the composition must lie (as in Figure 4.13a). Next we find the 'B' line. The intersection of these two lines at a point marks the composition of the mineral. As a final check, we can mark the 'C' line, which should pass through the same point (Figure 4.13b).

Question 4.2 Using the ABC ternary diagram in Figure 4.13c, determine the compositions indicated by the two points X and Y.

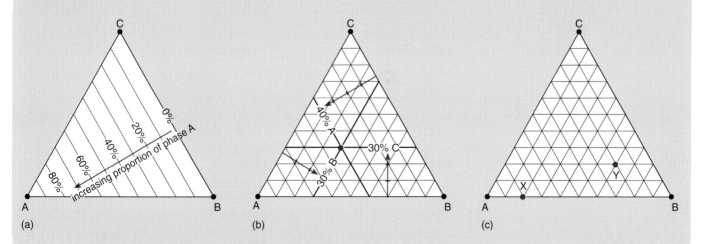

Figure 4.13 (a) A ternary diagram with three end-member components A, B and C. (b) A ternary diagram with the composition $A_{0.4}B_{0.3}C_{0.3}$ plotted. The percentages of the end-member components are indicated by the thick lines, which intersect at a point that shows the overall composition. (c) A ternary diagram for use with Question 4.2.

❑ Why do you think there is no solid solution between $KAlSi_3O_8$ and $CaAl_2Si_2O_8$?

■ For solid solution to occur, the exchangeable ions or atoms must have similar sizes and charges – otherwise large strains will build up in the crystal lattice, and the exchange becomes unfavourable.

For plagioclase feldspars: Ca and Na have similar sizes (about 0.1 nm) though they do differ in charge – but solid solution is possible if Al and Si are also exchanged.

For alkali feldspars: K and Na have the same charge, but differ in size by about 30%. Solid solution is just possible – at high temperatures.

However, there is also a large size difference between K and Ca (about 30%) *and* they differ in charge. Solid solution is therefore not possible.

Part of the idealized feldspar structure is shown in Figure 4.14. Al and Si lie at the centres of tetrahedra and, at high temperatures, are disordered. This means that there is a statistical probability of finding Al or Si in each tetrahedron (e.g., for orthoclase, the *occupancy* of each tetrahedron would be 25% Al and 75% Si).

Figure 4.14 Part of the tetrahedral framework for a feldspar mineral, showing the positions of symmetry elements. (This structure corresponds to the high-temperature form of feldspar.) The K, Na or Ca ions reside within the large, eight-sided cavities.

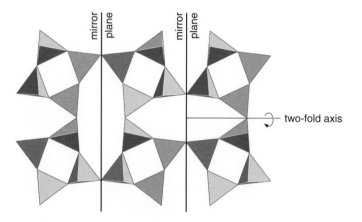

❑ Looking at the symmetry of the high-temperature feldspar structure in Figure 4.14, and with reference to Figure 2.10, which crystal system do you think it belongs to?

■ The combination of a two-fold rotation axis at right angles to a mirror plane is consistent with the monoclinic system.

As the temperature decreases, feldspars undergo a range of phase transitions involving:

• distortions of the tetrahedral framework;

• ordering of Al and Si atoms onto different tetrahedral sites.

❑ With reference to Figure 4.14, what would happen to the symmetry if Al and Si atoms became ordered onto different sites?

■ In the high-temperature, disordered structure, all the tetrahedra had the same statistical probability of containing Al or Si. With Al/Si ordering, tetrahedra would no longer be equivalent, as some would have a 100% probability of containing Si, and others would have a 100% probability of containing Al. Therefore both the mirror plane and the two-fold rotation axis would be destroyed. The crystal system would thus change from monoclinic to triclinic (Figure 2.10).

The tetrahedral framework has weak and strong directions. The weak directions are indicated in Figure 4.15a, and are defined by the eight-sided cavities. This results in two good cleavage planes. Their relationship to a three-dimensional crystal of feldspar is shown in Figure 4.15b.

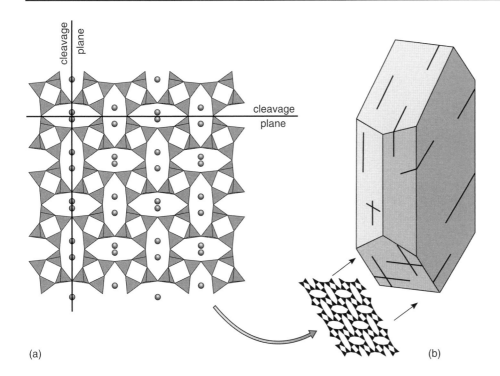

(a)

(b)

Figure 4.15 The presence of aligned cavities in the feldspar structure allows feldspar crystals to be cleaved in two directions at 90° to each other. (a) Portion of the tetrahedral framework, showing the directions of the planes of weakness. (b) Relationship between the structural weakness directions, and cleavage directions in a single crystal of feldspar.

TWINNING IN FELDSPAR

The presence of twins is a characteristic feature of feldspars. Twins can develop for two different reasons:

- because of a mistake during growth (growth twins);
- because phase transitions cause the symmetry to break down.

Growth twins are common in crystal structures that contain pseudo-symmetry – i.e., they contain similar, but non-identical directions. The presence of these structural similarities means that mistakes during crystal growth can occur without much increase in the energy of the crystal.

❏ Look at the feldspar crystal (MS VIII) in your Home Kit. You should be able to see that this crystal is twinned. What is the relationship between the two twin components? If your Home Kit specimen is not very good, try looking at the movie version of it on the 'Digital Kit' (on DVD 1).

■ The crystal contains two components, which are out of alignment with each other. The twin components overlap with each other (they are said to be inter-penetrant) and are related by a 180° rotation along the long axis of the crystal.

The feldspar structure *nearly* has a two-fold rotation axis along its crystallographic *z* axis. This results in a common kind of growth twin, especially in potassium-rich feldspar (K-feldspar) called a **Carlsbad twin**: two twin domains are related by a 180° rotation (Figure 4.16a) – which is the kind of twinning seen in the feldspar crystal in your Home Kit. (It is also possible to find other kinds of twin in feldspar crystals, such as the reflection twins indicated in Figure 4.16b.)

MS IX in your Home Kit is actually a rock containing large pink crystals of feldspar, and these show Carlsbad twins. If you tilt the specimen slightly you can get the light to reflect from first one half, then the other half of a twin component.

Figure 4.16 Twinning in feldspar.
(a) Twinning by rotation – the
example here corresponds to
Carlsbad twinning; (b) Twinning by
reflection. (c) An example of simple
twinning (two twin components) –
here twinned by reflection.
(d) Repeated twin components –
here twinned by reflection.

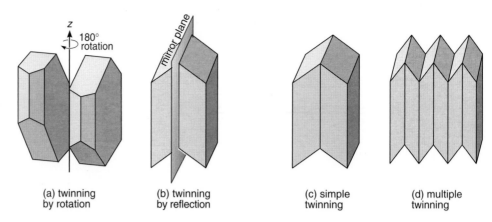

(a) twinning   (b) twinning   (c) simple   (d) multiple
by rotation   by reflection   twinning   twinning

❏ Would you expect to be able to see twinning in a thin section of a mineral,
when viewed with plane-polarized light?

■ Not normally. The differences between two twin components are very
slight, and unless you can see the outline of the crystal, there is nothing to
affect the plane-polarized light.

❏ What would happen when the section is viewed between crossed polars?

■ On either side of the twin boundary, there are different crystal orientations.
Therefore the indicatrix in one twin domain is in a different orientation from
the indicatrix in the other twin domain. So adjacent twin domains will not
go into extinction at the same time; as you rotate the microscope stage, first
one half of the twin will go dark, then the other half will go dark.

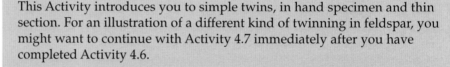

Activity 4.6

This Activity introduces you to simple twins, in hand specimen and thin
section. For an illustration of a different kind of twinning in feldspar, you
might want to continue with Activity 4.7 immediately after you have
completed Activity 4.6.

In addition to these simple twins, feldspar often shows repeated twinning
(Figure 4.16d) on a microscopic scale, which gives crystals a striped appearance.
This is sometimes referred to as **lamellar twinning**, and is a characteristic
feature of plagioclase feldspars.

One variety of K-feldspar, **microcline**, shows two kinds of repeated twinning in
thin section, with one set of twins arranged at 90° to the other set. The lamellar
twins overlap each other, giving a 'tartan' appearance. This is called **cross-
hatched twinning**.

Activity 4.7

This Activity introduces you to repeated twinning in feldspar.

4.7 NON-SILICATES

4.7.1 CARBONATES

The most common carbonate is the mineral **calcite** ($CaCO_3$). This is the major constituent of limestone rocks. You have already looked at the crystal structure of calcite in Section 3 (Figure 3.14). Calcite is a highly anisotropic mineral, with high-order interference colours. It is also quite a soft mineral (hardness 3) and has three excellent cleavages. These result from well-defined planes of weakness between the carbonate groups and the calcium ions.

Calcite is one polymorph of $CaCO_3$. There is another polymorph, called **aragonite**. Its crystal structure is slightly different from that of calcite, and it is less stable than calcite at ambient conditions. However, many marine organisms initially build their skeletons out of aragonite. When the animals die, their shells drop to the bottom of the ocean, and over time the aragonite transforms into calcite via a reconstructive phase transition.

4.7.2 OTHER NON-SILICATES

Two other important non-silicate minerals you are likely to meet are **haematite** (Fe_2O_3) and **pyrite** (FeS_2). Both are included as specimens in your Home Kit: haematite is MS XI and pyrite is MS I.

❑   With reference to Figure 4.1, what is likely to be the structural building block for the haematite structure?

■   Figure 4.1 shows that the molecular group involving iron and oxygen is the FeO_6 group. We might therefore expect haematite to contain FeO_6 octahedra.

Both haematite and pyrite have crystal structures containing octahedrally coordinated iron atoms. In the case of haematite, the structure consists of octahedral layers stacked on top of each other, giving a densely packed structure. (Each octahedral layer is a dioctahedral sheet, as shown in Figure 4.7b.)

Pyrite has a slightly different structure, with FeS_6 octahedra joined together by corner-sharing. Three octahedra meet at a point, i.e., each sulfur atom is shared between three iron atoms, making the overall formula of pyrite FeS_2. Activity 4.8 gives you an opportunity to explore the pyrite structure, and the structures of other rock-forming minerals.

Activity 4.8

This has been a very long section in which you have met many minerals in hand specimen and thin section. This multimedia Activity illustrates the crystal structures of some of the more important minerals.

You are not expected to memorize all of the properties of the rock-forming minerals; these are summarized on Bookmark 2. Using this as reference, you should be able to distinguish between the major rock-forming minerals, on the basis of their physical properties.

4.8 OBJECTIVES FOR SECTION 4

Now you have completed this Section, you should be able to:

4.1   Summarize the range of silicate mineral structures in terms of various degrees of SiO_4 polymerization.

4.2   Give examples of the essential structural features of the common rock-forming minerals: olivine, garnet, pyroxene, amphibole, mica, quartz, feldspar.

4.3   Give examples of some physical properties that can be attributed to specific crystal structural features.

4.4   Display a working knowledge of the basic chemistry and properties of rock-forming minerals in the Home Kit (with the aid of information summarized on the Block 2 *Bookmark*).

4.5   Display a working knowledge of the distinguishing features of the major rock-forming minerals in hand specimen (with the aid of information summarized on the Block 2 *Bookmark*).

Now try the following questions to test your understanding of Section 4.

Question 4.3   The structure of quartz is entirely built from SiO_4 units. Why then is its chemical formula SiO_2?

Question 4.4   The structures of the minerals olivine and silicate spinel (Mg_2SiO_4) are sometimes described in terms of close-packing of oxygen atoms. Close-packing is normally used to describe metallic structures. What are the similarities, and differences, between a metallic close-packed structure, and the structure of olivine? In terms of close-packing, how do the structures of olivine and silicate spinel differ?

Question 4.5   Quartz and mica are both silicate minerals, but they have very different cleavage properties. How do quartz and mica differ in cleavage, and why?

Question 4.6   What is solid solution? Give examples of two important rock-forming minerals that show solid solution.

Question 4.7   The term silica is used to refer to the chemical composition SiO_2. Is all silica quartz? What are silica minerals, and how do they differ from each other?

5   WHAT IS A ROCK?

In the remaining Sections of this Block, most of the Activities require you to refer to the rock (RS) and mineral (MS) specimens and thin sections (TS) from the Home Kit. Versions of all of these are also available on the 'Digital Kit' on DVD 1. When working your way through the Activities we would ideally like you to use all the materials at your disposal, though for various reasons you may find it difficult to do so on every occasion. How you use these materials is entirely up to you, though we feel that it is most important that you use the real Home Kit specimens as well as those on DVD. However, the latter may be extremely useful if you are unsure whether you are looking at a correct feature or detail on the real specimen. During Activities you will not be referred specifically to the specimens and thin sections on DVD, but please feel free to use them whenever you wish. Rock specimens are stored in the 'Rock Kit' and mineral specimens are stored on the 'Mineral Kit' on the 'Digital Kit'. Thin sections are stored on the separate 'Digital Microscope'. Static views of labelled thin sections are also stored in the 'Rock Kit' on the 'Digital Kit'.

Having studied the different properties and characteristics of minerals and how these are related to their internal structure and the way in which they are formed, we should now consider their importance with respect to the rocks within which they are found. From your study of Block 1 you will already be aware that there is a wide variety of rock types. In the following Sections we introduce you to the major rock types, their identifying characteristics and how to use these to deduce their mode of formation. We also look at the implications for the geological history of the area where the rocks occur. In other words, by accurate *observation* of a rock, it is possible to work out the *process* by which it was formed and hence interpret its *environment* of formation (the observation ⟶ process ⟶ environment concept introduced in Block 1, Section 1.1).

Activity 5.1

You should now watch the rest of the video sequence *Using the Microscope* on DVD 1, in which you are shown how to use the polarizing microscope to look at rocks in thin section and how to record the results of your observations.

A **rock** is a granular or interlocking aggregate of one or more types of crystal or grain. The following Sections introduce you to rock description and classification; be aware, though, that there is no unique pigeon-hole system for rock identification and that you may not always be able to give a precise name to a rock specimen. However, this does not matter; we would *much prefer* that you approach things in an analytical way, learning as much as possible from your own observations and interpretation, rather than just memorizing lists of names. Rocks can contain different minerals and, even in rocks containing the same few minerals, the relative proportions of these minerals may vary. Thus there is a huge variety of rock types, of which there are merely 27 in the Home Kit (Box 5.1). 'Instant recognition' can come only with practice, based on the continued application of the techniques you will learn in this course. Even experienced geologists are liable to make mistakes or need recourse to methods more sophisticated than those that can be considered here.

Rocks may be divided into three groups according to the way in which they are formed. Rocks that have crystallized from molten material or **magma**, either at the Earth's surface, after volcanic eruption (for example as **lava**), or beneath the surface, are known as igneous rocks. Weathering and erosion of pre-existing rocks at the Earth's surface yield a vast amount of rock and mineral particles or sediment that is subsequently deposited onto the surrounding land surface or into the oceans. Upon burial beneath further layers of sediment, these deposits become consolidated to give another important group known as the sedimentary rocks. The final group, known as the metamorphic rocks, are rocks that have been altered and recrystallized by heat and/or pressure at depth within the Earth. Under extreme conditions, metamorphic rocks can begin to melt and so produce new magmas.

Before examining the mineral composition of a rock it is often useful to examine its **texture**, because this can often give a clue as to its likely origin. Texture is the term used to describe the physical relationships between the particles from which a rock is made. Virtually all rocks have textures that are either crystalline

Box 5.1 Rock specimens in the Home Kit

The rock specimens in the Home Kit (subsequently referred to as RS 1, RS 2 etc.) are taken off large blocks collected from quarries or freshly broken surfaces of natural rock exposures. Some may have at least one flat sawn surface. They therefore look different from the weathered exposures and rock fragments that you might usually encounter in the field. To study the features of a rock properly, it is generally necessary to be sure that you are looking at a freshly broken, unweathered surface. Don't forget that all the specimens in the Home Kit are out of their natural context, which means that all you will know about their natural or field occurrence is what we may tell you. You will also discover that, in many cases, properties observed in a hand specimen are not sufficient to classify a rock completely; you may also need to examine it in thin section and to know its relationship with other rocks in the field setting.

or **fragmental**, but although useful, the interpretation of texture is not an infallible guide to rock type, as you will discover when working through the rest of this Block. However, we can use this broad textural classification as a convenient introduction.

In rocks with a crystalline texture, the minerals have grown together as aggregates of crystals that are interlocking; in most rocks with a fragmental texture, individual mineral and rock particles or grains have been transported and deposited and may be more or less rounded. Within both categories the size of individual fragments or crystals can vary considerably. Rocks with a crystalline texture are usually harder and more compact than those with a fragmental texture, and when they are broken they tend to fracture along cleavage planes *within* individual crystals rather than between crystals (Figure 5.1a). The result is that broken surfaces of such rocks show numerous flat surfaces that reflect and glint as they catch the light. Rocks with a fragmental texture usually fracture *between* individual grains (Figure 5.1b) but if the grains are very tightly held together, for example by a natural **cement** (a mineral that has precipitated from solutions within the rock), then they too may break across the grains.

Figure 5.1 Examples of the fracture patterns displayed by rocks with (a) crystalline texture and (b) fragmental texture.

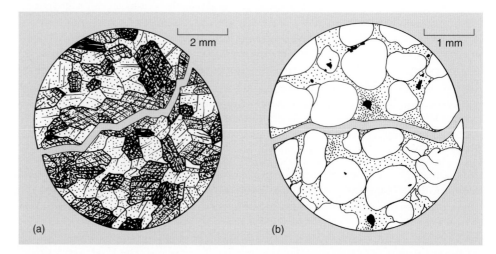

(a)   (b)

Activity 5.2

You should now do Activity 5.2, in which you are asked to examine some simple rock textures with a view to distinguishing between crystalline and fragmental textures in hand specimen and thin section.

Having made some simple observations of texture we can now consider to which major rock group these specimens belong. RS 19 consists of interlocking crystals in random orientations, which have grown together during crystallization from a magma. It is therefore an igneous rock. RS 12 is composed of a mixture of rounded and some more angular particles. Some of these particles are individual mineral grains and others are fragments of rock, indicating that this was once a sediment that has become consolidated to form a sedimentary rock. RS 4 has a crystalline texture and individual crystals within the rock are aligned in one direction. This is not a chance happening; the crystals are not derived from a liquid source but are the result of recrystallization or reorientation of earlier minerals in a pre-existing rock under conditions of intense, directed pressure. This rock, therefore, is metamorphic.

5.1 SUMMARY OF SECTION 5

1   Rocks are granular or interlocking aggregates of one or more types of crystal or grain.

2   Rocks contain minerals in different proportions, which leads to a huge variety of rock types.

3   Rocks may be divided into three main groups according to the way in which they formed: igneous, sedimentary and metamorphic.

4   Texture is the term used to describe the shape of the particles from which a rock is made and the physical relationship between them. In rocks with a crystalline texture, minerals have grown together as aggregates of interlocking crystals. In rocks with a fragmental texture, minerals and rock particles have been transported and deposited by water, wind or ice, and have become compacted and cemented.

5.2 OBJECTIVES FOR SECTION 5

Now you have completed this Section, you should be able to:

5.1   Recognize and appreciate the simple differences in origin and texture of an igneous, a sedimentary and a metamorphic rock.

5.2   Describe and explain the differences between crystalline and fragmental rock textures.

5.3   Recognize and describe simple rock textures using a hand lens and microscope.

6   IGNEOUS ROCKS

For centuries, people living near volcanoes have noticed that red hot molten rock that has erupted onto the Earth's surface as lava will cool and solidify to give solid rock. You may have been on holiday to the Canary Islands or Italy and visited the volcanoes there. Even if you have not visited a volcano, you will probably have seen spectacular shots of volcanic eruptions in TV programmes. However, rocks resulting from volcanic eruption (**extrusive** igneous rocks) represent only a small proportion of those rocks formed by the cooling and crystallization of magma, most of which occur at depth beneath the Earth's surface to form **intrusive** igneous rocks. By linking observations of texture, the sizes of crystals or grains (referred to as **grain size**) and mineral and chemical compositions with the geological setting in which the rocks are found, it is possible to describe and classify different rocks and to work out their mode of origin.

Extrusive rocks cool rapidly because they have erupted at the Earth's surface, but intrusive rocks cool more slowly within an insulating 'blanket' of surrounding rocks into which they have been emplaced. You have already met the concept of slow versus fast cooling in Section 2.1. In the case of the crystallization of magma, rapid cooling gives a fine-grained rock, which may even be glassy, whereas slower cooling gives a coarse-grained rock with larger crystals. Therefore the texture of an igneous rock is (usually) related to its cooling rate.

6.1 COOLING OF MAGMAS AND THE TEXTURE OF IGNEOUS ROCKS

As magmas cool and begin to solidify, the atoms from the liquid become organized into crystals of different mineral compositions. Any small disturbance in the melt, such as specks of impurity or slight turbulence, may be sufficient for the first tiny crystals to start to form. The crystals then continue to grow outwards in an ordered fashion by successive additions to their faces, whose geometry and orientation are controlled by specific planes of atoms in their structure (Section 2.2.5). Crystals that grow from these **nucleation centres** will generally be in random orientation relative to one another. The larger the number of nucleation centres, the more crystals will form. Sooner or later, crystals will grow into contact with one another to give irregular, interlocking boundaries, as in most of the igneous rocks in the Home Kit.

Activity 6.1

You should now do Activity 6.1, in which you will look at grain size in igneous rocks and what this might indicate about their cooling rates.

Figure 6.1 Top surface of columnar joints in a basalt lava flow, Staffa. Most are hexagonal, though some five-sided examples can be seen. Most are about 30 cm across.

RS 19 is a coarse-grained igneous rock known as **gabbro**. The Cuillin hills of Skye that you met in Block 1 (Activity 2.1) are composed of such a gabbro and represent the remains of a large reservoir of magma or **magma chamber** that possibly formed the root of a huge extinct volcano, now eroded away. RS 14 is the medium-grained equivalent of gabbro, known as **dolerite**; it crystallized more quickly in this example as an intrusive sill. RS 3 is the fine-grained equivalent of both the gabbro and dolerite, and is a **basalt**; basalts commonly form lava flows which, on cooling, may develop a spectacular polygonal pattern of **columnar joints** such as those found at Fingal's Cave on Staffa (Figure 6.1) and the Giant's Causeway in Northern Ireland (Plate 6.1).

We have seen that igneous rocks of similar mineral composition can have a range of grain sizes, from coarse (e.g. RS 19) to fine (e.g. RS 3). Though this may seem to be a fairly arbitrary classification, the criteria for describing grain size in igneous rocks may be quantified (Table 6.1). These classifications are made according to the *average* grain size of the **groundmass** or matrix minerals, and not on the size of any isolated large crystals that you may observe.

Table 6.1 Grain size criteria for igneous rocks. Note that the divisions are made according to the *average* grain size of the groundmass or matrix minerals.

coarse-grained	>2 mm	easily seen with naked eye
medium-grained	0.25–2 mm	easily seen with the hand lens
fine-grained	<0.25 mm	scarcely distinguishable, or indistinguishable, with the hand lens

Grain size in igneous rocks is partly determined by the number of nucleation centres per unit volume in a crystallizing magma. However, it is also related to the rate at which atoms are able to migrate towards these nuclei. The rate of formation of nuclei is lowest at high temperatures and highest at low temperatures (Figure 6.2a). However, the rate of diffusion of atoms is greatest at high temperatures and lowest at low temperatures (Figure 6.2b). In simple terms this means that if a magma cools slowly, although only a small number of nucleation centres may develop, the temperature remains high for long enough to allow comparatively long-range migration of atoms towards these nuclei with the subsequent growth of large crystals (as in RS 19).

❑ Under what conditions might such slow cooling of magma occur?

■ Slow cooling will occur if magma is intruded into rocks that are deep beneath the Earth's surface and might themselves be quite hot.

Conversely, if a magma cools quickly, a large number of nucleation centres may develop, but the decrease in diffusion rate will inhibit the migration of atoms towards them. Therefore crystals are numerous, but small (as in RS 3).

As a general rule, in most igneous rocks the coarser the grain size, the slower the cooling (i.e. at depth) and the finer the grain size, the faster the cooling (i.e. at or near the surface). With extremely fast cooling, crystals may not develop at all, in which case a glass will be formed (Section 2.1). Alternatively, the nucleation centres may be represented by tiny scattered crystals, whereas any remaining liquid will solidify as a glass (Plate 6.2).

❑ From Activity 3.3 in Section 3, can you remember the characteristic optical property of a glass under the microscope?

■ Glass (both natural and artificial) is isotropic, i.e. it remains dark (in extinction), when seen between crossed polars as the stage is rotated.

Plate 6.3 shows a rock, called **obsidian**, which consists entirely of natural glass. It is black and shiny with a characteristic curved or **conchoidal** (pronounced conk-oi-dal) fracture just like that seen in blocks of manufactured glass. You might think that if it is a glass it ought to be clear and colourless like manufactured glass; in fact, the black colour is thought to be due to small amounts of an impurity containing iron, which dramatically affects its colour, in much the same way as the colours in varieties of quartz are caused by small amounts of different impurities (Section 4.6.1 and Plate 4.1). Manufactured glass is an artificial silicate melt created from very pure silica sand, and hence not coloured, which has been cooled so rapidly that it has not crystallized at all. However, as was discussed in Section 2.1, glass is not particularly stable and will eventually crystallize (devitrify) with age; this can also be observed in natural glass such as obsidian.

The igneous rocks you have so far looked at have been even-grained or **equigranular**, the individual mineral grains in each rock being more or less the same size. However, in some igneous rocks, relatively large crystals or **phenocrysts** are set in a finer-grained groundmass. The texture of such rocks is described as **porphyritic**.

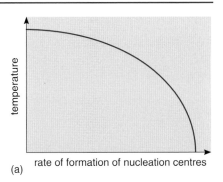

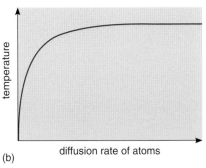

Figure 6.2 (a) A graph showing the increase in the rate of formation of nucleation centres as the temperature decreases. (b) A graph showing the decrease in the diffusion rate of atoms as the temperature decreases.

Activity 6.2

Now do Activity 6.2, in which you will explore the origins of phenocrysts in porphyritic igneous rocks and what this might tell you about their cooling histories.

6.2 MAGMA COMPOSITION AND MINERALOGY

Magmas are actually complex chemical mixtures, containing many elements that become distributed among several minerals as the magma crystallizes. Each mineral in an igneous rock usually begins to crystallize at a different temperature. It is not surprising, therefore, that igneous textures can be complex. The essential point to remember though is that a magma crystallizes over a *range* of temperatures and does not solidify all at once. This is particularly well illustrated in the porphyritic rocks (RS 1 and 6) that you examined in Activity 6.2; in these, the cooling rate must have been slow at first then more rapid. As a result, the minerals in the groundmass of a porphyritic rock will generally include those that make up the phenocrysts.

Porphyritic rocks have cooled in two stages: an initial slow cooling stage at depth producing the phenocrysts, followed by relatively rapid cooling at or near the surface producing the finer-grained groundmass.

Sometimes you may be able to deduce something about the order of crystallization of minerals in igneous rocks by examining a thin section. Plate 6.4 is a photograph of a rock similar to TS G from your Home Kit. You should be able to see plagioclase feldspar (rectangular crystals with first-order interference colours and lamellar twinning) and pyroxene (irregular and rather angular crystals, with low second-order interference colours).

❏   Why is it possible to say that at least some of the plagioclase crystallized *before* the pyroxene? (*Hint:* consider the distribution of plagioclase relative to pyroxene crystals.)

■   The irregular pyroxene crystals enclose long thin plagioclase crystals. As the magma cooled, therefore, at least some of the plagioclase must have formed *before* the pyroxene.

The answer to this last question illustrates a general rule regarding the crystallization history of an igneous rock:

> The observation that one kind of mineral has enclosed another shows that the enclosed mineral crystallized first.

You can also see in Plate 6.4 that the plagioclase crystals are both smaller and more numerous than the pyroxene crystals. However, the rock is not porphyritic because the pyroxene crystals are not large enough relative to the groundmass and did not grow much before the rest; indeed, in places the pyroxene crystals crystallized after the plagioclase. The magma probably cooled at a more or less steady rate from the time of intrusion to final solidification. For this rock, therefore, the same cooling rate must have resulted in *different* numbers of nucleation centres per unit volume for the plagioclase and the pyroxene.

The fundamental control on the mineral composition of an igneous rock is the chemistry of the magma from which it has crystallized. As a magma begins to cool, its composition will determine which minerals crystallize out first. As progressively lower temperatures are reached other minerals will begin to crystallize, and those minerals that crystallized at the higher temperatures may continue crystallizing or cease to form. The temperature ranges over which the main or **essential minerals** of igneous rocks generally form during the cooling of a magma are summarized in Plate 6.5.

Diagrams such as these are based on the results of laboratory studies of the conditions under which igneous rocks form. The 'lozenge' shapes give some idea as to the general importance of each mineral at a given temperature; the relative importance of each mineral in a crystallizing assemblage changes as the magma changes in temperature and, hence, composition. Where the widest part of a 'lozenge' lies within a rock field, the mineral is an essential mineral of that rock; any other minerals present in small amounts are called **accessory minerals**. You can see that the ranges for several minerals do not overlap at all (e.g. muscovite with pyroxene, or quartz with olivine). Where there is a gap between the temperature ranges of two minerals, those minerals are only exceptionally found together in igneous rocks. Thus olivine is hardly ever found with quartz or potassium feldspar. In contrast, minerals whose ranges of crystallization temperatures overlap are commonly found together, so that olivine, pyroxene and Ca-rich plagioclase feldspar form a predictable mineral association (as you have already seen in the rocks of Activity 6.1). The associations shown in Plate 6.5, therefore, are the basis of a simple igneous rock classification.

Activity 6.3

In Activity 6.3, you are asked to consider the nature of the groundmass minerals in a porphyritic rock and how their composition might relate to that of any phenocrysts present. You should do this Activity now.

In Activity 6.3, the use of mineral associations has helped us to make an informed prediction about the minerals that form the smallest crystals.

6.3 INTRUSIVE ROCKS

We have already introduced you to the general idea that intrusive igneous rocks are those formed by the slow crystallization of magmas, either at depth as large, irregular intrusions or plutons, or nearer the surface in cracks and fractures as shallow **minor intrusions** such as dykes or sills. You may remember from Block 1 that dykes are curtain-like igneous bodies that cut *across* pre-existing rock layers, i.e. they are discordant whereas sills are sheet-like and intruded *between* the layering in pre-existing rocks, i.e. they are concordant (Plate 6.6), although there may be an occasional discordant step (Figure 6.3). They generally represent offshoots from deeper magma chambers and may be associated with surface volcanoes and lava flows. You will learn more about the mechanisms for this in Block 3; in this Section we shall simply consider the nature of the rock types produced in terms of texture and mineralogy.

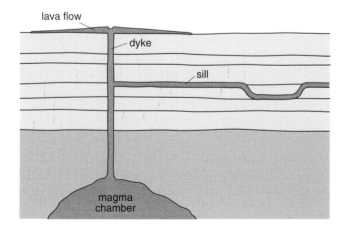

Figure 6.3 A schematic cross-section showing the difference between a dyke and a sill and their common association with a magma chamber at depth and surface volcanism.

When identifying and describing igneous rocks, or indeed any other type of rock, it is useful to be able to estimate the relative proportions of the minerals that they contain. This is most easily done using a thin section, but an estimate can also be made using a hand specimen if you are certain of your mineral identifications. The estimate is normally made only for the essential minerals. The procedure is to concentrate on one mineral at a time, in several fields of view, and to arrive at a semi-quantitative estimate of the proportion by volume of that mineral in the rock.

The estimation of proportions is important. It does take practice, so if you have difficulty at first, do not be too concerned. For fine-grained rocks in thin section this can be done by comparison with standard diagrams, as in Figure 6.4, which shows the area covered by a mineral for six given percentages. You can use these diagrams for direct visual comparison of the concentration of grains or crystals of the mineral that you are estimating.

Figure 6.4   Volume estimation diagrams for fine-grained rocks.

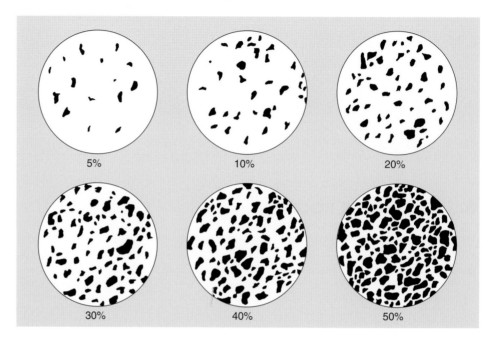

For coarser-grained rocks direct comparison may not be feasible, because too few grains may be in view at any one time. In this case, you should try to imagine that all the grains of a particular mineral (Figure 6.5a) are packed together into one (or more) quadrant(s) of the microscope field of view. Each quadrant is 25% of the field, so that if grains seem to fill about half of one quadrant, the mineral represents about 12% of the rock (Figure 6.5b). An alternative technique could be to look at the thin section between crossed Polaroid sheets (in the Home Kit), using the hand lens; this will enable you to use the volume estimation diagrams of Figure 6.4 directly, as for fine-grained rocks.

In coarse-grained, plutonic igneous rocks, all the minerals should be readily identifiable.

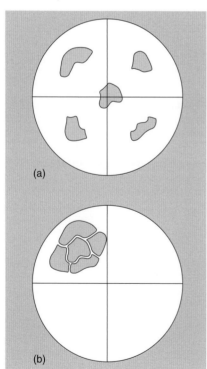

Figure 6.5   Volume estimation diagrams for coarse-grained rocks. (a) Mineral grains seen in one field of view. (b) The same grains 'packed' into one quadrant, about 12% of the rock.

Activity 6.4

You should now do Activity 6.4, in which you will look at examples of the three main plutonic rock types. Thin sections of these, taken from the 'Digital Microscope' on DVD 1, are illustrated in Plate 6.7, and at the end of this Activity you should be able to fill in the blank labels.

Plate 6.5 shows the ranges of composition in terms of the essential minerals for the main plutonic rock types. Note that the long plagioclase feldspar 'lozenge' indicates the gradational change in composition of plagioclase at different temperatures (and in different rocks), from Ca-rich (anorthite) at the highest temperature (gabbro), through intermediate varieties with similar amounts of Ca and Na in the structure (diorite), to Na-rich (albite) at the lowest temperature (granite). You were introduced to the concept of such solid solution by coupled substitution in plagioclase feldspars in Section 4.6.2. Thus, for instance, the essential minerals in a diorite are amphibole and plagioclase feldspar (intermediate in composition between the Ca- and Na-rich ends), with smaller amounts of biotite or pyroxene. Potassium feldspar also occurs in some diorites.

As you will see in Section 6.7, the boundaries between igneous rock types are fixed at arbitrary points in a continuous compositional range, which results in a great variety of igneous rock names. However, an understanding of these ranges of crystallization temperatures and mineral associations can help us to introduce some order into the complexity of these rocks.

Activity 6.5

You should now do Activity 6.5, in which you will look at another important coarse-grained rock from your Home Kit.

RS 23 is known as **peridotite**, and although not common at the surface, it is an important rock because it represents the mantle material underlying the Earth's crust. You will learn more about this in Block 3.

In Activity 6.4, we looked in some detail at the three main plutonic rock types. Because they are coarse-grained, we would expect them to have crystallized slowly at depth, as large igneous intrusions. As we have already mentioned, however, magmas of the same compositions may be intruded into cracks and fractures nearer the surface. The rocks formed are usually found as shallow minor intrusions, such as dykes or sills. Because they have cooled more rapidly than their plutonic counterparts, these rocks tend to be medium-grained in texture (Table 6.1). As you discovered in Section 6.1, the medium-grained equivalent of gabbro is dolerite. The medium-grained equivalent of diorite has the more logical name of **microdiorite**, and similarly the medium-grained equivalent of granite is **microgranite**. These terms are listed in Table 6.2, along with their volcanic, fine-grained equivalents. Any of these may also be porphyritic, and you have already met one such example in Activities 6.2 and 6.3 in RS 6 (thin section (TS) O). RS 6 contains phenocrysts of quartz and potassium feldspar (orthoclase) in a much finer-grained groundmass, the phenocrysts having crystallized more slowly in a magma chamber at depth before the magma rose and was intruded at shallower depths, any remaining liquid then crystallizing more quickly to form the groundmass. Although RS 6 has its origin in a shallow intrusion, the groundmass is so fine-grained (being largely unresolvable even with ×40 magnification) that it should be classified as a porphyritic rhyolite (Table 6.2).

Table 6.2 Rock names of common igneous rocks. Note that any of these rocks may also be porphyritic. For example, a basalt with phenocrysts would be called a 'porphyritic basalt'.

Average grain size of groundmass	Plutonic Coarse (>2 mm)	Shallow intrusive Medium (0.25–2 mm)	Volcanic Fine (<0.25 mm)
	gabbro	dolerite	basalt
	diorite	microdiorite	andesite
	granite	microgranite	rhyolite

6.4 VOLCANIC ROCKS

When magma erupts at the surface it may spill out as a lava flow (Plate 6.8a). Alternatively, as it solidifies it may become fragmented and be dispersed as fragments of various sizes (Plate 6.8b). When this fragmental debris eventually settles and becomes consolidated it will form a **pyroclastic** rock. The reasons and mechanisms for the different styles of eruption will be dealt with in more detail in Block 3, but differences in composition, mineralogy and crystallization temperature of different magmas have considerable influence on their eruptive style.

You have two examples of lava in the Home Kit. These are RS 1 (TS T) and RS 3 (TS I). You have already looked at these in Activities 6.2 and 6.1, respectively.

> **Question 6.1**   What evidence is there that these two specimens are volcanic in origin?

From Activity 6.1, you will remember that RS 3 (basalt) was the fine-grained, volcanic equivalent of RS 19 (gabbro). RS 1 is **andesite**, the fine-grained equivalent of RS 9 (diorite). The fine-grained equivalent for granite (RS 13) is **rhyolite**, although when magma of granitic composition finds its way to the surface it often erupts in an explosive fashion or becomes fragmented by other processes, which you will meet in Block 3, giving rise to a pyroclastic deposit.

Activity 6.6

You should now do Activity 6.6. In this Activity, you will look at some of the characteristic features of a pyroclastic rock in both hand specimen and thin section.

RS 25 is a pyroclastic rock, known as an **ignimbrite**. The sharp, angular outlines of individual minerals and the presence of igneous rock fragments, all in chaotic, random orientation, are evidence of the explosive nature of the eruption that gave rise to this rock. The glassy nature of the groundmass material indicates very rapid chilling, though the flow-like texture preserved within it indicates that the material must have been still very hot and 'plastic' before it became consolidated. You will discover more about the formation of ignimbrites and other pyroclastic deposits in Block 3.

6.5 PEGMATITES AND APLITES

At high pressures, silicate magmas can comprise up to 10% by mass of water (and gases such as fluorine), though more often the percentage is lower than this. On crystallization, some of this water becomes incorporated into **hydrous minerals** such as mica and amphibole. This means that they contain OH groups in their structures. However, many silicate minerals, in particular those that crystallize at high temperatures such as olivine and pyroxene, tend to be anhydrous, because their structures are not open enough to accommodate OH. Therefore, the proportion of water in a cooling magma inevitably increases as anhydrous minerals crystallize from it. If the concentration becomes too high, pressure is insufficient to keep it in the magma. In volcanic environments the water can escape as steam. Otherwise it will unmix to form droplets of a separate aqueous fluid. Fluid-enriched magmas are frequently squeezed into fractures in the surrounding rock or within the body of a pluton itself. The presence of an aqueous phase encourages the precipitation of very large well-formed crystals (such as MS VII in the Home Kit) on cooling. In some spectacular examples, crystals may be several metres in length. Mineral-filled fractures are described as **veins** and veins filled with such coarse-grained crystals are known as **pegmatites**. Although the term pegmatite refers to texture rather than composition, most pegmatites are of a similar composition to granite (Plate 6.9). It is important to realize that in pegmatites the large crystal size is *not* simply the result of slow cooling, but can be the result of crystals being able to grow relatively quickly to a large size, because the presence of aqueous fluids allows rapid migration of atoms towards nucleation centres. However, if the aqueous fluid is removed or escapes for some reason, sudden precipitation will lead to the formation of fine-grained equigranular veins, also of similar composition to granite; such veins are known as **aplites** (Plate 6.10).

6.6 AQUEOUS SOLUTIONS

Aqueous solutions themselves are important geological agents, particularly as they often give rise to a wide variety of valuable **ore deposits**. There is a complete gradation from solutions at ordinary temperatures, such as seawater, through warm solutions of circulating groundwater, as in mineral and hot spring areas, to hot solutions that are the by-products of magma crystallization, as discussed in Section 6.5. Aqueous fluids at temperatures above about 400 °C and at high pressure are highly reactive, and this enables them to dissolve minerals easily and to penetrate even the narrowest rock fractures. As the fluids migrate upwards along fractures in the surrounding rocks, away from the zone where they were heated, the temperature and pressure decrease, and the solubility of the dissolved material also drops. This results in precipitation of various minerals along the walls of the fractures to give mineral veins. The composition of these veins depends partly on the nature of the rock through which the fluids have passed before precipitation occurs and, in the case of fluids derived from magmas, also on the chemical composition of the magma and the distance from the source. The temperature of the fluids drops as the heat source cools; so first one mineral may be deposited along the sides of the veins followed by another towards the centre. This is because different minerals precipitate at different temperatures.

The most common types of vein are filled with either quartz (MS III and MS VII in the Home Kit) or calcite (MS IV in the Home Kit). Many quartz veins are formed from SiO_2 dissolved from sedimentary rocks that contain a high proportion of quartz, though some quartz veining is associated with SiO_2-rich magmas. Calcite is often derived from limestone to form veins, either within the limestone or in other adjacent rocks.

> **Question 6.2**   From what you can recall from Section 4, if you were to find yourself in the field trying to decide whether a vein was filled with quartz or calcite, how might you do this?

Veins may also contain economically important **ore minerals** such as **galena** (PbS), an ore of lead (MS VI in the Home Kit), sphalerite (ZnS), an ore of zinc (Figure 2.17), and molybdenite (MoS_2), an ore of molybdenum (Plate 6.11). These are generally much less common than simple quartz or calcite veining, although some areas may have a high proportion of economically significant mineral veins.

6.7 CHEMICAL COMPOSITION OF IGNEOUS ROCKS

So far, we have considered the importance of the composition of a magma in terms of the minerals produced when it cools and crystallizes. This is also a reflection of the chemical composition of the rocks thereby produced. Thus gabbro, dolerite and basalt all have the same minerals, as do diorite, microdiorite and andesite (but different from the first group). Members of each of these two groups of rocks also have the same overall chemical composition (different for each group), which, of course, is why the minerals within each group are the same.

The bulk chemical composition of a rock is found by crushing it to a fine powder and then analysing the powder to determine the abundance of elements present.* Most elements that appear in the analysis are contributed by more than one mineral. For example, granite consists of the following minerals:

- quartz, SiO_2
- alkali feldspar, $(K,Na)AlSi_3O_8$
- plagioclase feldspar, $NaAlSi_3O_8/CaAl_2Si_2O_8$
- biotite (mica), $K(Mg,Fe)_3AlSi_3O_{10}(OH)_2$

All these minerals contribute oxygen (O) and silicon (Si) to the total analysis. In addition, the alkali feldspar contributes potassium (K), sodium (Na) and aluminium (Al), whereas plagioclase feldspar contributes sodium, calcium (Ca) and aluminium. Biotite contributes magnesium (Mg) and iron (Fe), as well as potassium and aluminium.

Two examples of chemical analyses of igneous rocks are given in Table 6.3. We can use these analyses to illustrate some general principles about the chemical composition of rocks. Analyses are presented as oxides of the elements. This is a convention arising from the fact that the dominant element in all rocks is oxygen, as you can see by looking at the formulae of the minerals in granite. The relative proportions of oxides of different elements in chemical analyses reflect the relative proportions of the principal minerals in those rocks.

Table 6.3 Representative chemical composition[a] of a typical gabbro and granite. Note that iron can occur as Fe^{2+} or Fe^{3+}, which is why it is listed as two different oxides.

Oxide	Wt % oxide in gabbro	Wt % oxide in granite
SiO_2	48	70
TiO_2	2.5	0.5
Al_2O_3	15	15
Fe_2O_3	3	1
FeO	8	2
MgO	10	1
CaO	10	2.5
Na_2O	2	4
K_2O	1	3
H_2O	0.5	1

[a] The compositions are given as the percentages by weight (abbreviated to wt %) of the oxides.

It is important to realize, however, that the use of oxides in this way does not imply the presence of equivalent oxide minerals in the rock. For example, although the gabbro in Table 6.3 contains 48% SiO_2 (sometimes referred to as silica) there is unlikely to be any quartz or other silica mineral (whose formula also happens to be SiO_2) in the rock, because in gabbroic magma all the available SiO_2 is likely to combine with other elements to form Ca-rich plagioclase, pyroxene and olivine (Activity 6.1). In the granite however, there is enough SiO_2 left over after allocation to the feldspars and biotite for it to appear

---

* The usual method of analysing the powder is called X-ray fluorescence (XRF) spectroscopy. How it works is beyond the scope of this course.

as quartz. In general, rocks whose chemical analyses show less than about 60–65% SiO_2 are *not* likely to contain significant amounts of quartz, whereas those with *more* than 60–65% SiO_2 are quite likely to contain quartz, recognizable in hand specimen.

Although Si may occur as the oxide SiO_2, it is important to realize that, in igneous rocks, the elements Mg, Ca, Na and K *never* occur as oxide minerals, although some (but not most) Al, Fe and Ti may be found in oxide form as accessory minerals.

> **Question 6.3** According to Table 6.3, which oxide constituents are considerably more abundant in gabbro than granite?

> **Question 6.4** Which minerals are likely to account for the higher CaO content in gabbro than in granite?

> **Question 6.5** Which minerals are likely to account for the higher Fe_2O_3, FeO and MgO content in gabbro than in granite?

Silicates which have little or no iron or magnesium are called **felsic minerals**. The most common examples are quartz, feldspar and muscovite mica. We can see that the higher the SiO_2 content of an igneous rock, the greater will be the proportion of these minerals, so a granite may be called a **felsic rock**. Silicates which contain high proportions of iron or magnesium are called mafic minerals: the most common examples are olivine ($(Mg,Fe)_2SiO_4$) and pyroxene $(Mg,Fe,Ca)SiO_4$ (together with amphibole and biotite mica). Gabbro with its lower SiO_2 content has a higher proportion of these minerals and so a gabbro may be called a **mafic rock**. Rocks such as diorite, and its volcanic equivalent andesite, with a small amount of quartz (20% or less) are called **intermediate rocks**; they have an SiO_2 content correspondingly intermediate between that of granite and gabbro. Another group of rocks, including peridotite, which have even less SiO_2 than the mafic rocks, are known as the **ultramafic rocks**. In this classification, summarized in Table 6.4, it is important to remember that the rock types are defined in terms of their SiO_2 content, *not* on the amount of quartz present, although this can be an important visual clue.

Table 6.4 Classification of igneous rocks by SiO_2 and mineral content.

Wt % SiO_2	Type and example	Typical mineral composition
<45	ultramafic, e.g. peridotite	*no quartz;*
		dominantly mafic minerals; Ca-rich plagioclase minor or absent
45–52	mafic, e.g. gabbro	*no quartz;*
		rich in mafic minerals and Ca-rich plagioclase
52–66	intermediate, e.g. diorite	*between 0 and 20% quartz;*
		significant proportions of both felsic and mafic minerals; plagioclase contains roughly equal proportions of Ca and Na
>66	felsic, e.g. granite	*more than 20% quartz;*
		feldspars include both K-rich orthoclase or microcline and Na-rich plagioclase; mafic minerals approximately 25% or less

The relationship between SiO_2 in the analyses and relative proportions of different minerals is summarized for different kinds of igneous rock in Plate 6.12.

From Plate 6.12 you can see that ultramafic and mafic rocks with low SiO_2 contents contain a high proportion of mafic minerals, whereas felsic rocks with a high SiO_2 content contain mainly felsic minerals. This gradation applies regardless of grain size within the different groups of rocks (as you should recall from Activity 6.1). As Plate 6.12 would seem to indicate, there are no igneous rocks (apart from some pegmatites) with more than 75% SiO_2.

> **Question 6.6** A coarse-grained igneous rock has the chemical composition given in Table 6.5.
>
> (a) Is it a felsic, intermediate or mafic rock (Table 6.4)?
>
> (b) Can you predict what minerals may be present and the approximate volume percentage of each mineral?
>
> (c) What is the name of the rock?

Table 6.5 The chemical composition of an igneous rock, for use in Question 6.6.

Oxide	Wt % oxide
SiO_2	55
Al_2O_3	18
$FeO + Fe_2O_3 + MgO$	13
CaO	8
$Na_2O + K_2O$	5
H_2O	1

6.8 Summary of section 6

1   Most igneous rocks are formed when magma cools and crystallizes, either on the Earth's surface or beneath it, though some may form by fragmentation of solidifying magma.

2   Rapid cooling usually gives a fine-grained rock, which may even be glassy, whereas slower cooling usually gives a coarse-grained rock.

3   Crystals in an igneous rock form as a result of crystallization around nucleation centres in the originating magma.

4   Phenocrysts in a rock are indicative of crystallization during slow cooling followed by more rapid cooling.

5   The fundamental control on the mineral composition of an igneous rock is the chemical composition of the magma from which it has crystallized; different mineral associations are characteristic of different types of igneous rock.

6   Rocks with similar mineralogy and chemical composition, but different grain size, are derived from the same type of magma but have different cooling histories.

7   Intrusive rocks are formed by the cooling of magma beneath the Earth's surface.

8   Extrusive (volcanic) rocks are formed from magma that has erupted at the Earth's surface.

9   Pyroclastic rocks are the result of volcanic fragmentation of solidifying magma.

10 Pegmatites are the result of precipitation from a magma in the presence of a separated aqueous fluid phase. Aplites are the result of sudden precipitation from a magma when a separate aqueous phase is removed.

11 Veins are fractures filled with minerals that have precipitated from hot solutions often associated with igneous activity.

12 The proportions of oxides of different elements in chemical analyses reflect the relative proportions of the minerals in those rocks.

13 Igneous rocks may be classified as felsic, intermediate, mafic or ultramafic, according to their SiO_2 content.

6.9 OBJECTIVES FOR SECTION 6

Now you have completed this Section, you should be able to:

6.1   Identify the grain size and textures of fine-grained, medium-grained and coarse-grained porphyritic and glassy igneous rocks, and thereby interpret the relative rate of cooling of magmas from which they formed.

6.2   Recognize the common mineral associations of the igneous rocks.

6.3   Allocate a name to a given igneous rock on the basis of its grain size and mineral association.

6.4   Explain in general terms how the mineralogy of an igneous rock relates to its overall chemical composition.

6.5   Classify an igneous rock as felsic, intermediate, mafic or ultramafic on the basis of its SiO_2 content.

Now try the following questions to test your understanding of Section 6.

Question 6.7   Examine TS E and O in your Home Kit. Explain how we can say that the principal difference between these two rocks lies in their rates of cooling.

Question 6.8   A medium-grained igneous rock contains minerals in the proportions given in Table 6.6.

(a) Using information from Plate 6.12, what name would you ascribe to this rock?

(b) What would be the approximate SiO_2 content of a rock with this mineralogy?

(c) What names would you give to the volcanic and plutonic equivalents of this rock?

Question 6.9   A fine-grained igneous rock has the chemical composition given in Table 6.7.

(a) Use Table 6.4 and Plate 6.12 to decide whether the rock is felsic, intermediate, mafic or ultramafic.

(b) What minerals are likely to be present and in approximately what proportions?

(c) What is the name of the rock?

Question 6.10   Explain why an igneous rock containing 43% SiO_2 and 44% FeO + Fe_2O_3 + MgO in its chemical analysis is likely to contain a high proportion of mafic minerals.

Question 6.11   Give two reasons why you would classify granite as a felsic rock.

Table 6.6 The mineral composition of an igneous rock, for use in Question 6.8.

Mineral	Vol. %
quartz	7
potassium feldspar	7
plagioclase feldspar	58
biotite mica	7
amphibole	21

Table 6.7 The chemical composition of an igneous rock, for use in Question 6.9.

Oxide	Wt % oxide
SiO_2	48
Al_2O_3	17
FeO + Fe_2O_3 + MgO	19
CaO	12
Na_2O + K_2O	3
H_2O	1

7 SEDIMENTARY ROCKS

Most sedimentary rocks are derived by weathering and erosion of pre-existing rocks and are the result of physical, chemical and biological processes. Many are made up of mineral grains or rock fragments (collectively described as **clasts**) that have been transported by water, wind or ice, deposited in layers and then buried and consolidated. As a result, these have a fragmental texture (Section 5). Other sedimentary rocks originate from materials that are dissolved and later precipitated from freshwater or seawater to be either deposited by purely chemical processes or influenced by biological activities. These may have a fragmental or a crystalline texture, depending on their origin.

Physical weathering, by processes such as abrasion and the freeze–thaw action of frost and ice, produces small fragments of rock and mineral grains, whereas **chemical weathering** attacks minerals in rocks, by dissolution or chemical reaction, to produce alteration products, such as clay minerals (Section 4.5.2) and iron oxides. Quartz is more resistant to chemical weathering, and so it often remains after other minerals in a rock have been completely broken down. Insoluble aluminium, iron oxides and hydroxides also remain after a rock has been weathered away, but soluble products, such as sodium, calcium, potassium and magnesium ions, may be removed in solution by surface water or water percolating through the ground. These processes are summarized in Figure 7.1.

The combination of factors in weathering, transport and deposition determines the nature of the sedimentary rock finally produced. Because sediments are laid down in layers, visible bedding in rocks exposed in road cuttings and cliffs is often the first clue in the field that the rocks *may* be sedimentary (Plate 7.1); we should exercise caution here, however, because some volcanic rocks, notably basaltic lava flows and pyroclastic deposits, are also layered!

Figure 7.1 Weathering processes and their products.

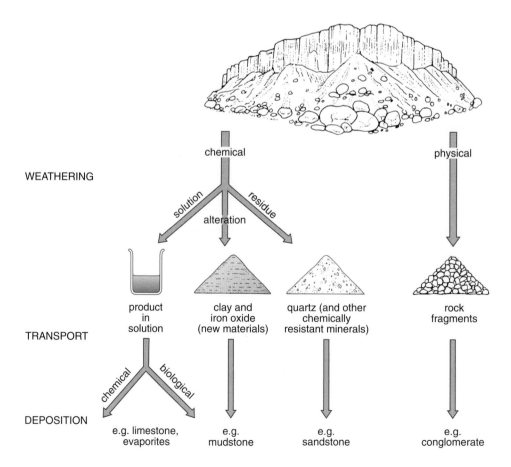

As sediments accumulate to progressively greater thickness, lower beds become compressed by the weight of overlying sediments. When these beds are compacted, their grains become packed more tightly, the spaces in between become greatly reduced in volume, and any water present is squeezed out. As it moves out, the water can dissolve and re-crystallize minerals as cement, which binds the grains together making a solid rock.

7.1 Siliciclastic rocks

The solid products of weathering are removed by erosion in streams and rivers, by glaciers or wind, and are transported, often over considerable distances. Rock and mineral fragments are often further broken down during transport itself. At the same time, chemically resistant mineral grains gradually become more rounded and less angular as they are abraded against other grains or the river bed, for example. For reasons you will learn about in Block 4, the final solid products of rock destruction are usually quartz or clay minerals. Deposits composed of these materials, which may also include grains of other silicate minerals, or even fragments of silicate-rich rock, are described as **siliciclastic**.

The ease with which a mineral grain may be transported or deposited by water or wind depends on its shape, size and density. In any particular transporting medium, there is a certain minimum size of particle that may be deposited for any flow speed; anything too fine will be carried away by the current and anything too coarse will be too heavy to be fetched in by the current. The result is that, given sufficient time and distance during transport, efficient separation of minerals and rock particles of contrasting size and density will occur, each group of particles being deposited at different points in the transport process. The result may eventually be an even-grained deposit composed of sand grains (RS 10) or clay grains (RS 27). This will be covered in greater detail in Block 4.

One important way in which siliciclastic rocks (and most other sedimentary rocks) may be described is based on their grain size. Grain size can be judged to a good approximation using a hand lens and a grain size scale. Figure 7.2 shows how you might do this using a few grains of salt, caster sugar and granulated sugar. Laying a few grains of each onto a piece of black paper and comparing them with the grain size scale, we can see that salt grains are equivalent to a fine-grained sand, caster sugar to a medium-grained sand and granulated sugar to a coarse-grained sand.

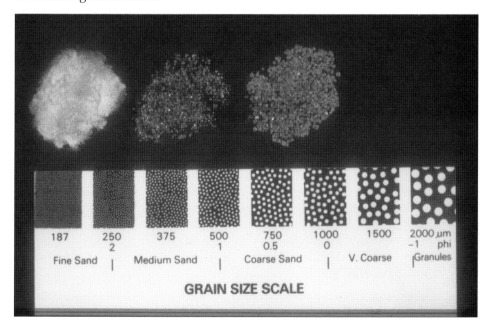

Figure 7.2   Use of the grain size scale to show difference in the size of grains of salt, caster sugar and granulated sugar.

Activity 7.1

You should now do Activity 7.1, which will enable you to practise the estimation of grain size in sedimentary rocks.

From Activity 7.1 you should have realized that in RS 7, 10 and 20 the grains are all about the same size, whereas RS 12 and 18 contain a wide range of grain sizes. This is because in RS 7, 10 and 20 the grains are **well sorted** by size (Figure 7.3a) as a result of persistent current activity during transport, or derivation from a rock with evenly-sized grains. In RS 12 and 18 a variety of grain sizes indicates that they are **poorly sorted** (Figure 7.3b). In poorly sorted sediments, and in sedimentary rocks, the spaces between large grains are usually infilled by finer-grained **matrix** material.

Figure 7.3 (a) Sediment with a narrow range of grain sizes (well sorted). (b) Sediment with a wide range of grain sizes (poorly sorted).

In a sedimentary rock it is the volumetrically most significant grains that determine its grain size classification. Although the rocks examined in Activity 7.1 have a range of grain sizes, in each the volumetrically most abundant grains are of sand size (from 62.5 μm to 2 mm); the general term for such rocks as these is **sandstone**. Coarser-grained sediments may vary in size from granules to boulders; on compaction and cementation this gives a **conglomerate** if clasts are rounded, or a **breccia**, if clasts are angular. Conversely, very fine-grained sediments may be either silt (from 4 μm to 62.5 μm), which on compaction and cementation gives a **siltstone**, or clay (<4 μm), giving a **claystone**. The term **mudstone** (RS 27) encompasses siltstones and claystones and those rocks containing a mixture of both clay- and silt-sized particles; if a mudstone splits easily into thin layers it may be classified as **shale**. Table 7.1 shows how siliciclastic rocks may be classified texturally on the basis of their grain size alone.

Sedimentary grains may also be described in terms of their sphericity, roundness, surface texture and the fabric they form within the rock. **Sphericity** is a measure of how closely the shape of a grain approaches that of a sphere. **Roundness** is concerned with the curvature of the corners of the grain: six categories, from very angular to well-rounded, are usually distinguished, as illustrated in Figure 7.4. Note that a grain may be well-rounded but not necessarily have a high sphericity, e.g. if the grain is shaped more like an ellipsoid. Sphericity and roundness may be grouped together as grain morphology.

Table 7.1 Grain size scale for siliciclastic rocks. Note that it is the volumetrically most significant grains in a sedimentary rock that determine its classification.

Grain size (most volumetrically abundant grains)[a]	Sediment name	Sedimentary rock name
>256 mm (very coarse)	boulders	
64–256 mm	cobbles	conglomerate (rounded fragments)
4–64 mm	pebbles	or breccia (angular fragments)
2–4 mm (coarse)	granules	
from 2 mm (medium) to 62.5 μm (fine)	sand	sandstone
62.5–4 μm	silt	siltstone ⎫
<4 μm (very fine)	clay[b]	claystone ⎭ mudstone (shale)

[a] μm = micrometre =10^{-6} m. The grain sizes in this table are arbitrary but not random: 256 mm is 2^8 mm, 64 mm is 2^6 mm, 62.5 μm is $(1/2^4)$ mm, and 4 μm is almost exactly $(1/2^8)$ mm.

[b] Clay can have two meanings: in terms of *grain size* clay refers to grains less than 4 μm in size; in terms of *composition* clay refers to certain types of sheet silicate mineral. However, most clay-sized particles in sedimentary rocks are, in fact, clay minerals.

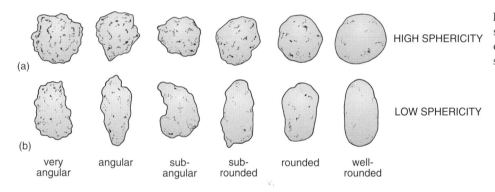

Figure 7.4 The morphology of sedimentary grains. For each category of roundness, grains of low and high sphericity are shown.

The **surface texture** of sedimentary grains can sometimes give a clue as to their origin or transport. Water-borne grains, such as might be found in rivers and on beaches, are often smooth and their surface glassy (like broken windscreen glass), whereas wind-blown grains, such as may be found in deserts, may be dull and frosted (like the surface of the glass in a sparkling wine bottle).

Figure 7.5 (a) Angular and glassy sedimentary grains from a beach sand. (b) Rounded and frosted sedimentary grains from a desert sand.

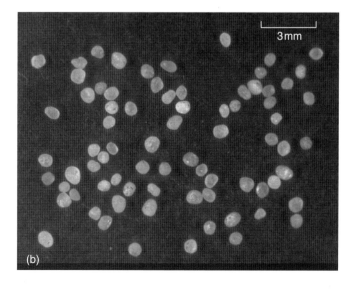

Sedimentary grains often display a particular **fabric** related to the orientation, packing and the nature of contacts between individual grains. If deposited in a current, clasts may be aligned with a particular preferred orientation. **Packing** describes the way in which sedimentary grains are stacked; grains of equal size will tend to be loosely packed, whereas grains of different sizes will be more closely packed, with smaller grains infilling the spaces between larger grains. If larger grains are in contact with each other, the fabric is described as **grain-supported** (like cherries in a jar); if larger grains are not in contact but seem to 'float' in finer matrix material, then the fabric is described as **matrix-supported** (like cherries in a Madeira cake). These textural terms will be more fully discussed in Block 4.

Activity 7.2

You should now do Activity 7.2. Sedimentary rocks contain a wide variety of grain types. This Activity gives you a chance to investigate the nature of the grains in the rocks you looked at in Activity 7.1.

From Activity 7.2, you should have realized that RS 7, 10 and 20 have a limited range of grain types, whereas RS 12 and 18 have a variety of grain types. RS 12 contains larger grains in a fine-grained matrix and is known as a **greywacke**. RS 18 is particularly rich in pink potassium feldspar, together with quartz and a few small rock fragments, and is known as an **arkose**: sandstone rocks are generally described as arkoses if they contain more than 25% feldspar. RS 7, 10 and 20 consist mainly of quartz and so are the end-products of the weathering process in which most physically and chemically unstable grains have been removed.

7.2 Carbonates

The **carbonate rocks** are the most widespread group of sedimentary rocks not of silicate composition. The most common examples are **limestones**, which are usually made of calcium carbonate ($CaCO_3$), in the form of calcite, but occasionally including a variety in which magnesium atoms are substituted for alternate calcium atoms, known as **dolomite** ($CaMg(CO_3)_2$). Most limestones are of biological origin, being the result of the extraction of calcium carbonate from seawater by tiny organisms that float just below the sea surface, or by animals such as clams, mussels, sea-urchins and corals, which use it to make their shells and skeletons. The skeletal remains of these organisms accumulate on the sea floor and become consolidated and cemented into limestones. As noted in Section 4.7.1, organic precipitation of calcium carbonate is often as the aragonite polymorph, which is subsequently transformed into calcite. Other limestones result from the direct chemical precipitation of calcite from freshwater or, more often, seawater. Because they are composed of calcite, most limestones will react by 'fizzing' with dilute hydrochloric acid to give off carbon dioxide:

$$CaCO_3(s) + 2HCl(aq) = CaCl_2(s) + CO_2(g) + H_2O(l) \qquad (7.1)^*$$

This is a useful diagnostic test for limestone in hand specimen and in the field. However, you should be aware that if the limestone consists of dolomite rather than calcite it will not react with dilute hydrochloric acid, unless its surface is deliberately broken into a powder.

---

* In this course, we use the common convention of showing the physical state of the reactants and products in a chemical reaction by inserting letters in parentheses: (s) means solid, (aq) means in aqueous solution, (l) means liquid, and (g) means gas.

Limestones are also very susceptible to chemical weathering because they dissolve easily in rainwater that has been acidified by the presence of atmospheric carbon dioxide. The dissolution of carbonates by water and dissolved carbon dioxide can be illustrated by the following equation:

$$CaCO_3(s) + H_2O(l) + CO_2(aq) = Ca^{2+}(aq) + 2HCO_3^-(aq) \qquad (7.2)$$

Exposed limestone surfaces become etched by this acid water along regular fractures or joints, to give a characteristic limestone 'pavement' (Block 1, Figure 2.16). In extreme cases this may give rise to extensive underground networks of potholes and caves (Block 1, Figure 2.18), such as are found at Cheddar Gorge in Somerset.

The textures of limestones are extremely variable. Many are obviously made up of shell fragments or skeletal remains; the collective term for these is **bioclasts**.

Activity 7.3

Bioclasts can be quite varied. You should now do Activity 7.3, in which you will be able to observe some good examples of bioclasts in limestones.

Another type of clast found in limestones is often the result of direct precipitation from seawater. Small rounded grains (called **ooids**) form aggregates that look rather like fish roe, to give an oolitic limestone. This has a distinctive appearance and may be quite easily recognized in hand specimen; RS 22 is a good example.

Activity 7.4

You should now do Activity 7.4. This Activity will give you the chance to examine oolitic limestone in more detail.

Another type of limestone with which you may be familiar is **chalk** (RS 8). This is well exposed along much of the eastern coast of the English Channel (the White Cliffs of Dover). It is a very fine-grained limestone made from the minute skeletal plates (or **coccoliths**) from untold numbers of tiny marine algae (Figure 7.6), which on death accumulated as a carbonate-rich mud on the sea floor and were then compacted during burial. Your specimen of RS 8 from the Home Kit may also contain some thin, buff-coloured marl bands; if not, then these can be seen in the chalk specimen in the 'Digital Kit' on DVD 1.

(a) 2 μm

(b) 2 μm

Figure 7.6 Highly magnified skeletal plates (coccoliths) of tiny marine algae in chalk: (a) complete cell coating of coccolith plates; (b) isolated coccolith from another species.

7.3 OTHER SEDIMENTARY DEPOSITS

During chemical weathering some minerals may be dissolved, but a given volume of solution can hold only a certain mass of dissolved mineral matter. If the volume of solution is reduced by evaporation then the concentration of dissolved mineral matter in solution increases and will eventually reach a saturation limit, at which point precipitation must occur. This process is carried out commercially in many hot countries, where the evaporation rate is high, to extract salt (NaCl) from the sea. The same process has occurred naturally under hot dry conditions in shallow basins many times in the geological past, leaving large salt deposits, which are economically important.

Sedimentary deposits formed in this way are known as **evaporites**. **Rock salt**, composed of the mineral halite (NaCl) (Figure 2.16), and gypsum ($CaSO_4.2H_2O$) (MS V), are two such evaporite minerals (Plate 7.2). Exposures of evaporites are not particularly common however, because they are very susceptible to re-solution by groundwater and are hardly ever found at the surface, except in dry climates. They also easily undergo recrystallization when buried, so that original textures are rarely seen.

Chemically or biologically precipitated rocks formed of silica are also found, many in association with limestones. Best known are the irregular lumps of **chert** (commonly referred to as flint) that are found within the chalk deposits of southern England (Plate 7.3). These are probably secondary in origin; that is, they have replaced part of the host rock by being precipitated from solutions derived from the silica-rich skeletons of marine plankton and sponges. Chert may also occur in bedded form, and is probably the result of accumulations of silica-rich skeletal material. These siliceous rocks are so fine-grained (microcrystalline) that individual grains cannot be distinguished even with the microscope. They break with sharp, conchoidal fracture surfaces, like broken glass, which is why many cultures have used them for the manufacture of axes, spears and arrow-heads.

Lumps such as flint that have grown by precipitation within a sediment are described as **nodules** (sometimes 'concretionary nodules' or 'concretions'). If not composed of silica they may be some kind of carbonate mineral. The conditions required to cause nodules to grow are complex and not well understood, but often a nodule is found to have formed around a particular object, such as a fossil. It is important to distinguish between nodules and pebbles; pebbles have usually been brought in by a strong current whereas nodules grow *after* deposition and tell us nothing about the conditions under which the sediment accumulated.

In swamps and bogs, where water is stagnant and where organic, carbon-rich matter, particularly plant material, accumulates faster than it decays, **peat** will be formed. If this is then buried deeply and compressed it will eventually form **coal**. Coal is dense and black and usually so thoroughly altered that plant remains may only rarely be seen.

7.4 MINERAL ASSOCIATIONS IN SEDIMENTARY ROCKS

As you have now discovered, the processes of weathering, erosion, transport and chemical precipitation ensure that most sedimentary rocks are composed of quartz, clay minerals or calcite. If the processes continue long enough and conditions are right, these constituents may be so efficiently separated that virtually pure sandstones, mudstones or limestones are formed.

However, it takes a long time for this separation to be achieved, and conditions of sedimentation may not be favourable, so that many sedimentary rocks consist of a mixture of these three minerals in various proportions. This is shown schematically as a ternary diagram in Figure 7.7, where each corner of the triangle represents 100% of one of each of these minerals. The names given to sedimentary rocks formed by various mixtures of each of these minerals are also shown. Rocks composed mainly of quartz and calcite lie along the left-hand edge of the triangle in Figure 7.7. The name given to such a rock will depend on the relative proportions of quartz and calcite in it, from limestone through sandy limestone and calcareous sandstone to a pure quartz sandstone. Similarly, there is a range of rocks from quartz sandstone to mudstone along the right-hand edge of the triangle, and between mudstone and limestone along the bottom edge (a calcareous mudstone or muddy limestone is commonly referred to as a **marl**).

The middle part of Figure 7.7 corresponds to sedimentary rocks with more or less equal amounts of quartz, calcite and clay minerals. Hence a limestone containing significant amounts of both quartz and clay minerals could be called a sandy muddy limestone.

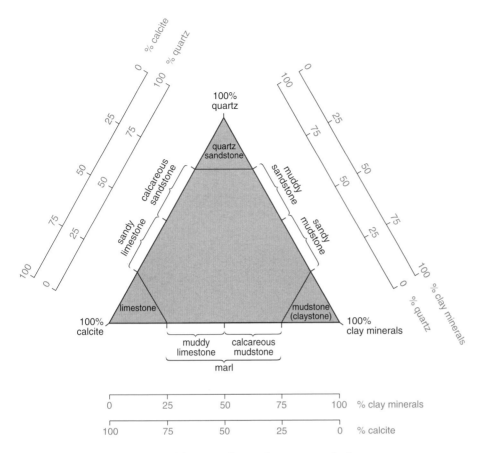

Figure 7.7 Ternary diagram to show the relative proportions of the principal minerals in common sedimentary rocks. (Refer to Box 4.1 if you have forgotten how to read a ternary diagram.)

Question 7.1 What would you call a rock composed of:

(a) 60% clay minerals and 40% quartz?

(b) 60% quartz and 40% calcite?

(c) 40% clay minerals and 60% calcite?

Figure 7.7 is somewhat simplified because, as you know from Activity 7.2, there are other components of sedimentary rocks that are not represented on it. The most important of these are rock fragments, feldspar, mica (muscovite being more common than biotite in sedimentary rocks), iron oxides and organic matter. The formation of rocks such as RS 12 (greywacke) and RS 18 (arkose) will be dealt with in Block 4. A sandstone with a significant amount of mica could be described informally as a micaceous sandstone. Because of its flaky nature, mica is often blown away from sediments deposited by the wind; its presence in a sedimentary rock is therefore a useful indication of deposition in water.

Question 7.2 Which of the rocks that you investigated in Activity 7.2 might you describe as a micaceous sandstone?

Now look at RS 15 with a hand lens. You should be able to see a lot of small mica flakes catching the light on bedding surfaces.

❑ Would you classify RS 15 as a micaceous sandstone?

■ No; the overall grain size is too fine, according to Table 7.1, for it to be called anything other than a mudstone (or shale if it splits quite easily along bedding planes).

The ways in which the products of weathering and erosion are eventually transformed into sedimentary rocks are summarized schematically in Figure 7.8, which shows the important routes of the different components through the processes of sedimentary rock formation covered in this Section. Compaction and the precipitation of cement from percolating groundwater begins at

Figure 7.8 A diagram summarizing how the solid and dissolved products of rock weathering and erosion accumulate as different kinds of sediment, which are then compacted and cemented to form new rocks.

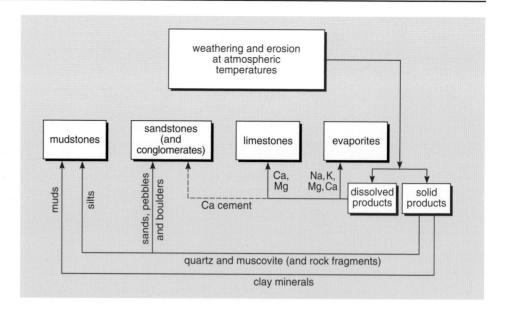

ordinary atmospheric temperatures but, as we shall see in Section 8, at temperatures above about 200 °C, and often with increased pressure, a whole new group of rocks may form as a result of metamorphism.

7.5 CHEMICAL COMPOSITION OF SEDIMENTARY ROCKS

When classifying sedimentary rocks, the texture and mineral composition are generally more useful than the chemical composition. As you might expect, however, the chemical analyses reflect the minerals present. Table 7.2 shows typical chemical analyses of a sandstone, a claystone and a limestone. The data are expressed in the form of weight per cent of oxides, but (as for igneous rocks) this is merely a useful convention and does not necessarily reflect the actual presence of these oxides as separate minerals.

Table 7.2 Typical chemical compositions for some sedimentary rocks.

Oxide	Wt % in sandstone	Wt % in claystone	Wt % in limestone
SiO_2	78.4	58.5	2.1
TiO_2	0.25	0.66	0.06
Al_2O_3	4.8	15.5	0.81
Fe_2O_3	1.1	4.1	0.54
FeO	0.3	2.5	–
MgO	1.2	2.5	7.9
CaO	5.5	3.1	42.6
Na_2O	0.45	1.3	0.05
K_2O	1.3	3.3	0.33
P_2O_5	0.08	0.17	0.04
H_2O	1.6	5.0	0.77
CO_2	5.0	2.7	41.6
elemental carbon	–	0.81	3.1
Total[a]	99.8	100.1	99.9

[a] Chemical analyses commonly do not add up exactly to 100% because the techniques of analysing for 12 or so elements are complex and small errors are unavoidable. Good chemical analyses are regarded as those that total between 99.5 and 100.5%.

Question 7.3   To which minerals would you attribute:

(a) the high SiO_2 content in sandstone?

(b) the high Al_2O_3 content in claystone?

(c) the high CaO and CO_2 content in limestone?

7.6 SUMMARY OF SECTION 7

1   Sedimentary rocks are the result of deposition of the products of physical and chemical weathering.

2   Siliciclastic rocks are derived from the solid products of physical and chemical weathering.

3   A simple classification of siliciclastic rocks is based on the size of their constituent grains.

4   The shape and surface texture of sedimentary grains may give a clue as to their origin or transport.

5   Carbonate rocks, commonly referred to as limestones, are almost entirely composed of calcite ($CaCO_3$) or, less commonly, dolomite ($CaMg(CO_3)_2$) and are usually the result of biochemical or chemical precipitation from seawater.

6   Evaporites are deposits formed as a result of evaporation of water from shallow basins under hot dry conditions.

7   Chert (including the variety commonly referred to as flint) is a precipitated form of microcrystalline silica (SiO_2).

8   In stagnant boggy conditions, carbon-rich plant material will accumulate to give deposits of peat and coal.

9   The processes of weathering, erosion and transport ensure that most sedimentary rocks are composed of a mixture of quartz, clay minerals and calcite in various proportions, though other components may include rock fragments, feldspar, mica (usually muscovite), iron oxides and organic matter.

10 For sedimentary rocks, the texture and mineral composition are more important for classification than the chemical composition, although chemical analyses reflect the minerals present.

7.7 OBJECTIVES FOR SECTION 7

Now you have completed this Section, you should be able to:

7.1   Recognize the common groups of sedimentary rocks on the basis of their textures, mineralogy and composition.

7.2   Allocate a name to a sedimentary rock on the basis of its texture and mineralogy.

7.3   Describe the different textural attributes of sedimentary grains.

7.4   Relate textures and mineral associations in the sedimentary rocks to their mode of origin.

7.5   Explain, in simple terms, weathering processes and the effect of these upon the nature of sediments produced.

Now try the following questions to test your understanding of Section 7.

Table 7.3 The chemical composition of a sedimentary rock, for use in Question 7.6.

Oxide	Wt %
SiO_2	60
Al_2O_3	16
$FeO + Fe_2O_3$	7
MgO	4
CaO	3
$Na_2O + K_2O$	5
H_2O	5

Question 7.4   Why do you think it might be that muscovite survives weathering better than biotite? (*Hint:* consider the chemical compositions of the two minerals.)

Question 7.5   Which minerals would you expect to find in sediments derived from the following rocks: RS 10 (TS W), RS 13 (TS E), and RS 19 (TS K)?

Question 7.6   A sedimentary rock has the chemical composition given in Table 7.3. Comparing it with Table 7.2, what sort of rock might it be, and what would you expect the main mineral to be?

8 METAMORPHIC ROCKS

When rocks are subjected to an increase in pressure or temperature, or both, they can recrystallize in the solid state (i.e. without melting) and new minerals and textures will result. Such changes are said to be the result of **metamorphism** and the new rocks formed are known as metamorphic rocks. Metamorphic rocks may be produced from igneous or sedimentary rocks, or even from pre-existing metamorphic rocks. In some instances, metamorphic changes may be minor, and features of the original rock may still be recognized. In most cases, however, the rock changes so much that the identity of the original rock cannot be determined.

Question 8.1   What are the most likely causes of increased heat or pressure that might lead to metamorphism?

Metamorphism resulting from the intrusion of hot magma into colder rocks is known as **contact metamorphism** and this is usually limited to the area immediately surrounding an igneous intrusion. Metamorphism resulting from an increase in pressure (almost inevitably accompanied by an increase in temperature) is known as **regional metamorphism** and, as the name suggests, may affect vast volumes of rock. A less common form of metamorphism occurs in areas of intense local deformation, such as in faults. Here temperatures and pressures are low, although the fault movements themselves can cause localized frictional heating; this type of metamorphism is called **dynamic metamorphism**. This will be dealt with in more detail in Block 3.

8.1 CONTACT METAMORPHISM

This is perhaps the simplest kind of metamorphism. When hot magma is intruded into colder rocks they become 'baked' by heat dissipated from the intrusion. The term **hornfels** is applied to *any* hard, splintery rock that results from 'baking' in contact metamorphism and is a purely textural rather than compositional term.

An everyday analogy might be the manufacture of pottery. Soft clay pots are transformed (metamorphosed) into hard and brittle objects by firing in kilns at temperatures of 1000 °C or more. This analogy illustrates three fundamental aspects of the metamorphism of rocks:

- Changes usually occur in the solid state without melting (although some melting *may* occur under extreme conditions).
- There is usually no significant change in the overall chemical composition, although water and gases may be lost.
- The chemical elements that make up the original minerals (clay minerals in our 'pots' example) are redistributed into new crystal structures. Any new minerals produced are stable at higher temperatures.

Since contact metamorphism (also known as thermal metamorphism) is the result of heat alone, it typically occurs in the absence of strong deformation. New minerals may form and these normally grow in random orientation so that contact metamorphic rocks, such as hornfelses, break with an irregular fracture, as do pots fired in a kiln. When these randomly oriented minerals grow large enough, the rock takes on a 'spotted' appearance (Plate 8.1). The zone of metamorphic rocks around an igneous intrusion is known as a **metamorphic aureole**.

8.2 REGIONAL METAMORPHISM

Regionally metamorphosed rocks are formed under the influence of increased pressure, as well as increased temperature, so that their mineral constituents are often lying with their long axes more or less parallel to one another. Minerals will recrystallize in this way in order to minimize the effect of compression (Figure 8.1); this applies particularly to those minerals that typically form platy (flat) crystals (e.g. mica) or elongate crystals (e.g. amphibole).

The term **foliation** is applied to the alignment of platy minerals; the term **lineation** describes the alignment of elongate minerals (Figure 8.2).

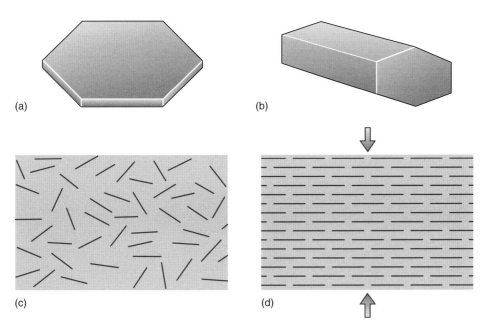

Figure 8.1 Examples of platy and elongate crystals and the way these become aligned in metamorphic rocks: (a) a platy mica crystal; (b) an elongate amphibole crystal; (c) a random aggregate of mica or amphibole; (d) the alignment of platy or elongate crystals under the influence of compression.

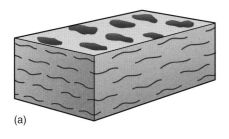
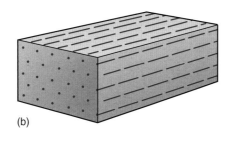

Figure 8.2 Simplified diagrams to illustrate (a) the alignment of platy minerals to produce foliation and (b) the alignment of elongate minerals to produce lineation. Most regionally metamorphosed rocks show foliation; many also show lineation.

Activity 8.1

You should now do Activity 8.1, which gives you the opportunity to examine foliation and lineation in metamorphic rocks from the Home Kit.

Rocks such as RS 26 that are medium- or coarse-grained and rich in mica, defining an often undulating foliation (or **schistosity**), are called **schists**. RS 16 also has a schistosity, but because it consists predominantly of the mineral amphibole, in this instance we can further classify it as an **amphibolite**. However, apart from a few exceptions of this kind, metamorphic rock terminology is quite simple because it is descriptive of the texture of the rock.

Small-scale migration of chemical elements in some regionally metamorphosed rocks causes the felsic and mafic minerals to be segregated into distinct bands, the alternating bands having various thicknesses; this is known as **metamorphic banding**. The bands are not always sharply defined and may grade into one another. A medium- or coarse-grained, banded metamorphic rock is known as a **gneiss** (RS 4), though some schists may also exhibit mineral segregation.

Question 8.2 Looking at RS 4 with the hand lens, and, checking its thin section (TS H) if necessary, identify the mineral that makes up the darker bands in this rock.

In regionally metamorphosed rocks, the degree of development of foliation and banding is used with grain size to describe the texture of the rock. In general, under the least amount of metamorphism, in fine-grained rocks very closely spaced, flat foliation planes are formed, to give a **slate**. Slate is often used commercially for roof tiles because it can be so easily split along these foliation planes, which are often referred to as cleavage or **slaty cleavage**. You should note, however, that such rock cleavage, which is the result of mineral alignment in metamorphic rocks, is different from cleavage in minerals, the latter being planes of weakness in the crystal structure of the minerals (Section 2.5.5).

As the temperature and pressure of metamorphism increase, foliation surfaces become more widely separated as grain size increases through **phyllites** to schists. Foliation surfaces also often become folded to give a characteristic 'wrinkled' appearance, particularly in phyllites. Slates or phyllites are produced only from rocks that were originally fine-grained and sedimentary in nature (such as mudstone); if a basalt or a sandstone were to be metamorphosed under the same conditions it would show few obvious signs of metamorphism, except maybe under a microscope. In particular, a coarse-grained rock would not develop a slaty cleavage. A gneiss will form from rocks that include only a small proportion of platy (mica) minerals. Hence gneisses are usually formed from strongly metamorphosed igneous rocks, or mica-poor sedimentary rocks. Under extreme conditions of regional metamorphism, a schist or a gneiss may lose its foliation or banding, the felsic and mafic minerals becoming separated into more patchy domains to form a rock known as a **migmatite** (Plate 8.2). With further melting of a metamorphic rock, a magma will be released, which, on cooling, will solidify to form an igneous rock.

In general, the coarser the grain size of a metamorphic rock, the more extreme the conditions (i.e. the higher the temperature and/or pressure, and the longer the time period) under which metamorphism took place. Note that this is a totally different explanation for grain size from that for igneous rocks, in which the grain size is related to cooling rate. The terms used to describe regional metamorphic rocks are summarized in Table 8.1.

Table 8.1 Major textural groups of regional metamorphic rocks.

Textural type	Nature of foliation	Grain size	RS number (to be filled in during Activity 8.2)
slate	very closely spaced, almost perfectly flat foliation surfaces	fine (<0.25 mm)	
phyllite	characteristics between slate and schist with a sheen of minute mica and chlorite flakes on wrinkled foliation surfaces	fine (<0.25 mm)	
schist[a]	moderately spaced undulating foliation surfaces, characteristically with abundant mica	medium (0.25–2 mm) to coarse (>2 mm)	
gneiss[a]	widely spaced undulating foliation surfaces with bands of felsic and mafic minerals	medium (0.25–2 mm) to coarse (>2 mm)	
migmatite	patchy domains of felsic and mafic minerals (see Plate 8.2)	coarse (>2 mm)	

[a] This should not be taken to imply that there is a progressive change from schist to gneiss with increased metamorphism, because a schist is usually too rich in mica.

Activity 8.2

As you have just discovered, regionally metamorphosed rocks exhibit a number of different textures according to the pressure and temperature at which they were formed. You should now do Activity 8.2, in which you will examine these different textures.

8.3 GROWTH OF PORPHYROBLASTS

When you were looking at RS 26 in Activity 8.1 you probably observed that, as well as abundant muscovite, the rock also contains some large pinkish-red garnet crystals. Many of these are larger than the average grain size and they are quite well-formed, with several flat faces developed on each crystal, just as in MS X in the Home Kit (though you may have noticed that MS X is a green variety of garnet and not pinkish-red in colour). Large crystals such as these in metamorphic rocks are called **porphyroblasts** and rocks containing them are termed **porphyroblastic**. (Do not confuse with the term phenocrysts. Porphyroblasts are formed in the solid state during metamorphism.)

> **Question 8.3** From Section 6, can you remember how phenocrysts form? What is the textural term for a rock containing phenocrysts?

Although RS 26 is a rock formed by regional metamorphism, porphyroblasts may also grow in rocks affected by contact metamorphism (Plate 8.1). When porphyroblasts form, the main factor that controls grain shape and size is the **surface energy** of the mineral (defined as the energy needed to increase the surface area by unit area). In general, the greater the surface energy of a mineral, the greater the strength with which atoms are held together at the crystal surface and the more likely the mineral is to form large and well-shaped porphyroblasts in a metamorphic rock.

> **Question 8.4** If you look at RS 26 with the hand lens, you can see that the matrix surrounding the garnet porphyroblasts consists mainly of muscovite mica together with some glassy quartz, although this is less easy to see. Which of these three minerals do you infer to have the highest surface energy?

> **Question 8.5** MS I in the Home Kit comprises porphyroblasts of metallic-looking pyrite contained within a fine-grained metamorphic rock. What is this rock?

8.4 CHEMISTRY AND THE CONTROL OF MINERALS IN METAMORPHIC ROCKS

Metamorphism normally involves little or no change in the overall chemistry of a rock, apart from the expulsion of aqueous fluids and gases. However, the individual minerals within a metamorphic rock are *not* usually the same as those that were present in the parent rock before metamorphism; for instance the chemical elements that make up the clay minerals in a claystone may become redistributed as mica on metamorphism. With further increases in temperature and pressure, other minerals may develop, such as the garnets you have seen in RS 26. A wide range of minerals may form during metamorphism, depending on the chemistry of the original rock, and the temperature and pressure of metamorphism. This will be discussed further in Block 3.

There are some rocks, however, in which no new minerals are formed by metamorphism. These are rocks made entirely of quartz, or entirely of calcite. Rocks consisting mainly of a single mineral are termed **monomineralic**. In these two examples the only elements involved are Si and O in quartz and Ca, C and O in calcite. During metamorphism, crystals of quartz or calcite simply grow and fuse together by transfer of material in the solid state from the original sedimentary grains.

❏ Which rocks consist entirely of (a) quartz and (b) calcite?

■ Figure 7.7 shows that rock (a) could be a quartz sandstone and rock (b) could be a limestone.

A quartz sandstone will become a **quartzite** upon metamorphism and a limestone will become a **marble**. Neither quartz nor calcite normally forms platy or elongate crystals when growing within a rock, so quartzites and marbles do not develop foliation or lineation and the individual grains are in random orientation with a granular (or **granulitic**) texture. This means that it may be difficult in practice to identify them as metamorphic unless the field relationships are known. Because these rocks may equally be the product of contact metamorphism or regional metamorphism, it is important to take field relationships into account.

Activity 8.3

The development of a granulitic texture is a feature of monomineralic rocks that have undergone recrystallization during metamorphism. In Activity 8.3 you will examine two examples of monomineralic metamorphic rocks from the Home Kit.

It is apparent, therefore, that one of the primary controls on the minerals that form during metamorphism is the chemical composition of the parent rock. Other factors controlling the nature of new minerals that develop are temperature and pressure. Because the source material may be so varied, many of these minerals are only found in metamorphic rocks. You will learn more about this in Block 3.

If we consider the progressive metamorphism of one particular kind of parent rock, such as a mudstone, then the minerals that crystallize during various degrees of metamorphism will depend only on the temperature and pressure. At low temperatures and pressures, the new minerals that form from the clay minerals and fine-grained quartz of mudstone are chlorite and muscovite. As the temperature and pressure increase, some of these early formed minerals themselves begin to be transformed into new minerals, e.g. chlorite will change into biotite. These in turn may give way to other minerals, as you will see in Block 3.

At the same time as new minerals form, the development of foliation and metamorphic banding allows the textural classification outlined in Table 8.1 and Activity 8.2; here you can see that there is an associated increase in average grain size with increased metamorphism. Eventually, if the temperature becomes high enough, the rock may begin to melt, forming a migmatite. If metamorphism ceases at some point and the rock becomes exposed at the Earth's surface, we can see an association of minerals which tells us at what point metamorphic development ended. These associations are called **metamorphic assemblages**, and, as we have seen, their nature depends on overall rock composition, temperature and pressure.

❑ Look again at RS 26. Which minerals are present?

■ The main platy mineral that defines the foliation is mica, and the large pinkish-red porphyroblasts are garnet. You may also be able to see some glassy quartz crystals, more obvious on the sides of the specimen showing the 'edges' of the foliation surfaces.

The assemblage of this rock is, therefore, garnet-mica-quartz, and it was probably derived by metamorphism of a mudstone. From its texture we can call it a schist, so it might be more accurately described as a garnet-mica-quartz schist. This name is somewhat cumbersome, however, and so in a rather simpler way we can refer to this rock as a garnet-mica schist, using the names of the porphyroblastic mineral and the dominant foliation mineral only.

Therefore, as far as foliated, banded or lineated rocks are concerned, the procedure for naming them is to identify the textural type (slate, phyllite, schist or gneiss), and then add a prefix to this, with the names of one or more of the principal minerals of which they are composed.

> **Question 8.6** Suppose that interbedded amongst some mudstones (e.g. RS 27) there was a basalt (e.g. RS 3) lava flow. Explain whether or not you would expect the mineral assemblage produced by metamorphism of the basalt to be the same as that produced by metamorphism of the mudstones.

Activity 8.4

You should now do Activity 8.4. In this Activity you are asked to consider the effects of regional metamorphism on different rock types.

The mineralogical changes in rocks of various compositions during progressive regional metamorphism are summarized in Figure 8.3. It shows the trends during these processes rather than the absolute temperatures at which the various changes occur. It is important to note that for metamorphism of mudstones the temperatures shown on the vertical axis are those of the *formation* of the minerals shown. Once formed, a mineral will often persist to much higher temperatures. Also, since both temperature *and* pressure control the formation of new minerals, Figure 8.3 cannot be used to decide the exact temperature at which a particular rock was formed. The composition of the original rock is also important: a metamorphosed mudstone will usually form a schist, whereas a metamorphosed granite will usually form a gneiss.

Figure 8.3 Mineralogical changes in progressive regional metamorphism of typical mudstones, sandstones and limestones.

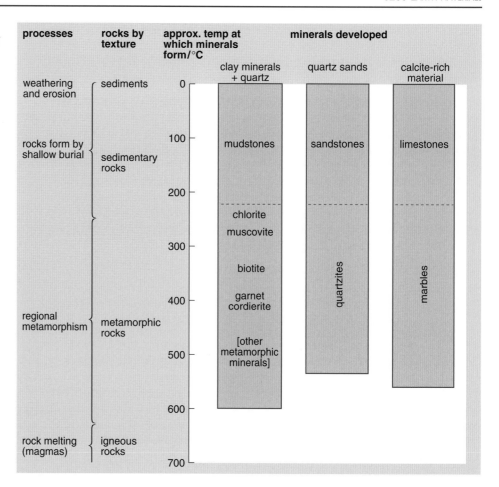

8.5 SUMMARY OF SECTION 8

1 Metamorphic rocks are formed from pre-existing rocks by recrystallization in the solid state (without melting) as a result of an increase in pressure or temperature, or both.

2 Contact metamorphism occurs when hot magma is intruded into colder surrounding rocks.

3 A rock affected by contact metamorphism may be described as a hornfels if it has become hard and splintery as a result of baking, or spotted if new minerals have grown with a random orientation.

4 Regional metamorphism occurs in rocks that have been affected by an increase in pressure and temperature so that the long axes of their constituent minerals are lined up more or less parallel to one another to give a foliation or lineation; this occurs in order to minimize the effect of compression.

5 With higher pressures and temperatures, felsic and mafic minerals may become segregated to give the rock a banded appearance.

6 In regionally metamorphosed rocks, the degree of development of foliation and banding is used with grain size to describe the texture of the rock.

7 Under extreme conditions of regional metamorphism a rock may begin to melt to form a migmatite.

8 Metamorphism normally involves little or no change in the overall chemistry of a rock, apart from the expulsion of aqueous fluids and gases, although the individual minerals within a metamorphic rock are not usually the same as those that were present in the parent rock before metamorphism.

9 One of the primary controls on the minerals that form during metamorphism is the chemical composition of the parent rock; other factors are temperature and pressure. Together these give an association of minerals, known as a metamorphic assemblage, which can be used to infer the conditions under which metamorphism occurred.

8.6 OBJECTIVES FOR SECTION 8

Now you have completed this Section, you should be able to:

8.1   Describe the differences between contact and regionally metamorphosed rocks.

8.2   Identify the metamorphic textures of regional metamorphism and account for the growth of porphyroblasts.

8.3   Recognize the common mineral associations of metamorphic rocks.

8.4   Explain in general terms how the mineralogy of a metamorphic rock depends on the chemistry of the original rock from which it is derived.

Now try the following questions to test your understanding of Section 8, and then do Activity 8.5.

Question 8.7   Examine RS 11 and 26. Why can you say that RS 26 probably formed under more extreme metamorphic conditions than RS 11?

Question 8.8   Compare RS 26 with the rock containing MS I. What are the similarities and differences between these two rocks? Which was produced under the more extreme conditions of metamorphism?

Question 8.9   Explain why at first sight you might misidentify RS 17 as an igneous rock. How would you recognize its true nature when you looked at its mineral content?

Activity 8.5

As you have now completed your study of the three main rock groups and how these might be identified, you should watch the video sequence *Rocks in the field* on DVD 1. In this video sequence you are introduced to the way in which rocks may be examined in the field (*in situ*) and how information thus obtained may be used to make a simple interpretation of the geological structure and history of a field locality.

9 THE ROCK CYCLE

Rocks are continually being formed and destroyed by geological processes. These processes form a complex set of inter-relationships, described as the **rock cycle** (Plate 9.1).

The rock cycle relates the three rock groups to each other, to surface processes such as weathering, transport and deposition, and to internal processes such as magma generation and metamorphism. You will learn more about these processes in Blocks 3 and 4. Weathering and erosion are closely linked to another important cycle known as the water cycle, or **hydrological cycle**, which governs the movement and availability of water at the Earth's surface. The main source of energy for the hydrological cycle is heat from the Sun (Figure 9.1).

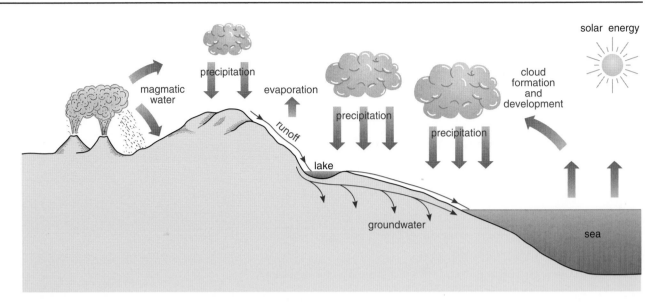

Figure 9.1   The hydrological cycle.

Weathering and erosion produce sediments that are transported by water, wind and ice, either across the land surface, or from the land eventually into the oceans. These sediments may then become compacted and cemented into sedimentary rocks. Such rocks may be uplifted and exposed at the Earth's surface once again, in which case they will be weathered and eroded to give new sedimentary rocks. However, if they are subjected instead to an increase in pressure or temperature, or both, they will be transformed into metamorphic rocks. This transformation may be the result of deep burial or compressive forces associated with plate collision and mountain building. If metamorphic rocks are then heated to extremely high temperatures they may actually melt to give magma; this will rise within the crust and, on solidification, produce igneous rocks. However, metamorphic rocks may be uplifted and exposed at the Earth's surface *before* melting can occur. Igneous and metamorphic rocks exposed at the surface will be weathered and eroded to give sedimentary rocks once again.

You can thus appreciate that the rock cycle is actually rather complicated and that individual rocks may be the product of a number of different processes. These processes are inter-related and lead to a continuous recycling of the materials that comprise the Earth's crust and uppermost mantle. We will explore the igneous and metamorphic aspects of the rock cycle in Block 3.

9.1 SUMMARY OF SECTION 9

1   Rocks are continually being formed and destroyed by geological processes; these include weathering, erosion and deposition, magma generation and metamorphism, all of which are linked together within the rock cycle.

2   Weathering and erosion are also linked to the hydrological cycle, which governs the movement and availability of water at the Earth's surface. The hydrological cycle is driven by heat from the Sun.

9.2 OBJECTIVES FOR SECTION 9

Now you have completed this Section, you should be able to:

9.1   Explain the concept of the rock cycle.

9.2   Relate the three major rock groups to their relative positions in the rock cycle.

ANSWERS TO QUESTIONS

Question 1.1

(a) The number of atoms required to cover 1 mm is given by:

$$1 \text{ mm}/0.16 \text{ nm} = 1 \times 10^{-3} \text{ m}/1.6 \times 10^{-10} \text{ m} = 6.3 \times 10^6$$

i.e., over 6 million per millimetre!

(b) If in 1 millimetre there are 6.3×10^6 atoms, then in 1 metre there will be $6.3 \times 10^6 \times 10^3 = 6.3 \times 10^9$ atoms. A cubic metre can be expressed as $1 \text{ m} \times 1 \text{ m} \times 1 \text{ m}$, so the number of atoms required to fill 1 m^3 is given by:

$$(6.3 \times 10^9) \times (6.3 \times 10^9) \times (6.3 \times 10^9)$$

$$= 2.5 \times 10^{29}$$

$$= 250\ 000\ 000\ 000\ 000\ 000\ 000\ 000\ 000\ 000$$

(which is quite a lot).

Question 2.1

(a) The pressure is 0.05 MPa. The water/steam phase boundary passes through the point with x coordinate 50 °C, and y coordinate: 0.05 MPa.

(b) The 'triple point' at which ice, water and steam coexist is defined by the intersection of the three phase boundaries: ice/water, ice/steam, and water/steam. Measured on Figure 2.2, this corresponds to a temperature of 6 °C and a pressure of 0.03 MPa.

Question 2.2

The new mineral could belong to any crystal system except the cubic system. A stretched-out shape is not consistent with cubic symmetry. Cubic crystals have similar shapes in all three dimensions.

Question 2.3

The mineral's hardness is 6. The hardness must be greater than that of window glass (5.5), and less than that of hardened steel (6.5).

Question 3.1

We use the relationship

birefringence = retardation/thickness

The retardation is 550 nm = 550×10^{-9} m (your own retardation may be slightly different, depending on the interference colour you have observed), and the thickness is 30 μm = 30×10^{-6} m. Thus

$$\text{birefringence} = \frac{550 \times 10^{-9} \text{ m}}{30 \times 10^{-6} \text{ m}} = 0.018$$

Question 3.2

The mineral is probably isotropic, and hence belongs to the cubic system. (Note that, in some rare cases, it is possible to observe an anisotropic crystal that has its optic axis perpendicular to the thin section – and such a crystal would also appear to be isotropic.)

Question 3.3

An anistropic mineral has two permitted vibration directions. If the crystal is rotated so that one permitted vibration direction is parallel to the polarizer direction, then all the light passing through the crystal will vibrate parallel to this direction. The relief seen will depend on the refractive index for this vibration direction. At 90° to this direction, all the light will vibrate parallel to the other permitted vibration direction, and the relief seen will depend on the other principal refractive index for this section.

If there is a large change in relief as the stage is rotated, then the two refractive indices must be very different – i.e., the mineral has a very high birefringence. This mineral is therefore highly anistropic, and should display a high-order interference colour.

Question 3.4

Diamond has a cubic structure (strong bonds in all directions), and so will be optically isotropic. It is a relatively dense structure (Table 2.1), and so it is expected to have a high refractive index. (The high refractive index of diamond causes the 'fire' of the gemstone.) Diamond crystals would therefore show very high relief in plane-polarized light, and would appear dark in all orientations when viewed between crossed polars.

Graphite has a layer structure with strong bonds within each layer, but weak bonds between successive layers. One would therefore expect a large difference between the refractive index for light vibrating parallel to the layers, and light vibrating perpendicular to the layers. Graphite is therefore predicted to be highly anistropic, and might show high-order interference colours when viewed between crossed polars. (In fact, graphite usually appears opaque – but when very thin flakes are cut, it shows a deep blue colour.)

Question 4.1

If we draw a vertical line through the 300 °C mark on the temperature axis in Figure 4.11, it cuts the stishovite/coesite phase boundary at a pressure of 8 GPa. Thus, if a sample of silica were held at 300 °C and a pressure of 8 GPa, or higher, it would be converted into stishovite.

Question 4.2

The composition represented by point X is 80% A and 20% B ($A_{0.8}B_{0.2}$). The composition represented by point Y is 20% A, 60% B, and 20% C ($A_{0.2}B_{0.6}C_{0.2}$).

Question 4.3

Quartz has a fully polymerized structure with each SiO_4 tetrahedron connected to four other tetrahedra. In a polyhedral model, the tetrahedra *share corners* (i.e., each oxygen atom is shared between two tetrahedra). So although each silicon atom is bonded to four oxygen atoms, it has to share each oxygen atom with another silicon. This makes the ratio of silicon to oxygen 1 : 2, and hence the chemical formula for quartz is SiO_2.

Question 4.4

In a close-packed metal structure, the metal atoms (ions) behave like hard spheres, in contact with each other, and held together by free electrons. This is not quite the case in olivine: the oxygen atoms are arranged similarly to metal atoms, that is, in hexagonal layers, stacked in an ABAB sequence. However, the oxygen atoms are not directly in contact with each other; there is no metallic bonding, and the oxygen atoms are instead bonded to silicon, magnesium and/or iron atoms, which reside in interstices between the oxygen layers.

Silicate spinel has the same chemical composition as olivine, but the oxygen layers are arranged differently, giving an ABCABC stacking sequence. Thus, the arrangement of oxygen atoms in olivine is analogous to hexagonal close-packing, and the arrangement in spinel is analogous to cubic close-packing.

Question 4.5

Cleavage is caused by differences in the strengths of bonding along different directions, or planes, in the crystal structure. The quartz structure (Figure 4.9b) has strong Si–O bonds in all directions, with no preferentially weak directions. Quartz therefore has no cleavage; when struck with a hammer, a quartz crystal breaks into random and irregular fragments. In contrast, the mica structure (Figure 4.8) has very different bonding in different directions. There are strong bonds within the layer sandwiches. However, the bonding between adjacent sandwiches is much weaker. This results in distinct planes of weakness between the structural sandwiches, and hence mica shows near-perfect cleavage.

Question 4.6

Solid solution refers to the range of chemical composition possible for a given crystal structure. Solid solution involves the substitution of one or more atoms or ions, at specific sites in the crystal structure. For example, olivine can range in composition from pure Mg_2SiO_4 to pure Fe_2SiO_4 – with a continuous spread of solid solution compositions in between, with Mg substituting for Fe, and vice versa. Other examples of solid solution series include the plagioclase feldspar series (from anorthite, $CaAl_2Si_2O_8$ to albite $NaAlSi_3O_8$) and alkali feldspar series (from albite $NaAlSi_3O_8$ to potassium feldspar, $KAlSi_3O_8$).

Question 4.7

There are many different phases of silica, including solid forms and liquid. The silica phase diagram (Figure 4.11) shows a number of different solid phases. These have the same chemical composition, but different crystal structures (i.e., silica has a number of polymorphs). The crystal structures for the different polymorphs involve different kinds of arrangement of SiO_4 groups – although one phase, stishovite, has SiO_6 octahedral groups. To convert one silica polymorph (e.g., quartz) into another (e.g., stishovite) requires the breaking of many bonds – and a reconstructive transformation.

Question 6.1

They are both fine-grained, with randomly oriented, interlocking crystals (obvious only in thin section for RS 3), indicating rapid cooling from a magma, probably as a result of eruption at the Earth's surface. RS 1 may appear slightly more coarse-grained, but as discussed in Activity 6.2, this is due to the presence of small phenocrysts that crystallized within the magma at depth *before* it erupted.

Question 6.2

Calcite (MS IV) has a hardness of 3 and so can be scratched with a penknife, whereas quartz (MS VII) has a hardness of 7 and so cannot be scratched with a penknife. In fact, quartz will leave a scratch mark on any steel. Also, calcite will 'fizz' with dilute hydrochloric acid, because calcite is a carbonate and will react with the acid to give off carbon dioxide (see 'acid test' in the 'Properties of Minerals' on DVD 1 (Block 2 Earth Materials). You will find the chemical reaction spelt out in Section 7.2. Quartz is a silicate and will not react with dilute acid.

Question 6.3

The oxides Fe_2O_3, FeO, MgO, CaO and TiO_2 are more abundant in gabbro.

Question 6.4

Plagioclase feldspar (Section 4.6.2) and pyroxene (Section 4.4.1) both have Ca-rich varieties.

Question 6.5

Pyroxene and olivine, since they are both mafic minerals (Section 2.5.2).

Question 6.6

(a) From Table 6.4, the SiO_2 content of 55% tells us that the rock falls into the intermediate category.

(b) From Table 6.4 we can eliminate quartz as a major constituent straight away. This is supported by Plate 6.12, which shows that the dominant mineral will be plagioclase feldspar of intermediate composition (i.e. containing roughly equal amounts of Ca-rich and Na-rich components) with lesser amounts of mafic minerals, such as pyroxene and amphibole.

The volume percentage of plagioclase can be found from the vertical scale at the left of the diagram. You can do this using Figure A6.1: the volume percentage of plagioclase in this rock will be approximately $95 - 35 = 60\%$. By the same reasoning, we may expect the rock to contain about 35% of mafic minerals, made up from about 20% of pyroxene, 15% of amphibole and a little biotite. It may also contain a small amount (about 5%) of potassium feldspar and quartz, although not enough to see in hand specimen and probably not easy to see even in thin section.

(c) By now you should have realized that the rock cannot be anything but a diorite (Plate 6.5). If it had been a medium-grained rock of this composition it would be called a microdiorite and if fine-grained it would be called an andesite (Table 6.2).

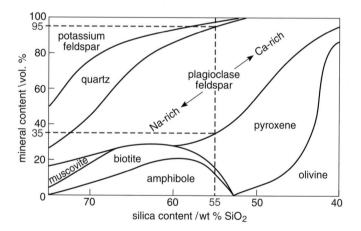

Figure A6.1 Solution for Question 6.6b.

Question 6.7

Both rocks are crystalline and igneous. They contain the same principal minerals, that is, quartz and potassium feldspar (microcline in TS E, orthoclase in TS O). As they have similar compositions, they must have crystallized from magma of roughly the same composition.

The coarse and relatively even-grained (equigranular) texture in TS E is the result of slow cooling, which enabled large crystals to grow. However, in the rock represented by TS O, the large crystals (phenocrysts) formed during a period of slow cooling at some depth beneath the surface, whereas the fine-grained groundmass formed during more rapid cooling, after the magma had been subsequently intruded near to the Earth's surface.

Question 6.8

(a) Using the method outlined in the answer to Question 6.6b, you should have been able to work out that a medium-grained rock with this mineralogy would be a microdiorite (Figure A6.2).

(b) The silica (SiO_2) content of such a rock would be approximately 60 wt % (Figure A6.2). [*Comment*: we chose the mineral proportions of this rock to fit exactly the relative proportions in Plate 6.12. Be aware, however, that in nature there is some degree of variation. For example, another rock could exist with 10% biotite and 11% amphibole, but with the other minerals in the same proportions as in the first rock. This second rock would not be an *exact* match to any composition in Plate 6.12, but would have *roughly* the same SiO_2 content, and the same rock name, as the first rock.]

(c) The volcanic equivalent of a microdiorite is andesite and the plutonic equivalent is diorite (Table 6.2)

Question 6.9

(a) Both Table 6.4 and Plate 6.12 tell us that the rock is mafic (48% SiO_2).

(b) By the method outlined in the answer to Question 6.6b (Figure A6.1), the minerals are likely to be: Ca-rich plagioclase feldspar (100 − 68 = 32%), pyroxene (68 − 8 = 60%) and olivine (8 − 0 = 8%).

(c) The rock is fine-grained, so it is a basalt (Tables 6.2 and 6.4).

Question 6.10

At 44%, the percentage of FeO + Fe_2O_3 + MgO in this rock is very high, much higher than in, say, basalt (e.g. Question 6.8). Rocks containing such a high proportion of these elements must be rich in mafic minerals. The percentage of SiO_2 is very low (43%), which tells us that it can contain no quartz; Table 6.4 and

Plate 6.12 confirm this. As it is an igneous rock we would call it ultramafic.

Question 6.11

As you can see from Table 6.3, granites have more than 66% of SiO_2 in their chemical analyses which places them in the felsic category. From Plate 6.12 you can see that granites contain about 25% quartz and are rich in feldspar; altogether they contain at least 75% felsic minerals, which again classifies them as felsic rocks.

Question 7.1

(a) Sandy mudstone; (b) calcareous sandstone; (c) muddy limestone or marl.

Question 7.2

RS 20 (TS J) might be informally described as a micaceous sandstone because it is composed primarily of quartz but has distinctive layers of colourless muscovite mica and brown, pleochroic biotite mica. Note that the presence of biotite in this rock is curious, since biotite, being a mafic mineral, is usually more susceptible to chemical weathering.

Question 7.3

(a) Quartz (SiO_2); (b) clay minerals (Section 4.5.2, Figure 4.8); (c) calcite ($CaCO_3$).

Question 7.4

Felsic minerals, such as muscovite, often survive chemical weathering and are quite commonly found in sedimentary rocks, particularly those deposited in water (Section 7.4). Mafic minerals, such as biotite, are more susceptible to chemical weathering and so only rarely survive in sedimentary rocks.

Figure A6.2 Solution for Question 6.8a.

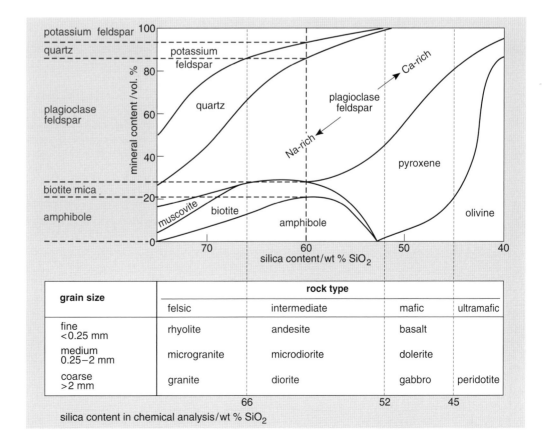

Question 7.5

RS 10 is the easiest one of these to deal with. Sediments formed from this rock would simply consist of recycled quartz grains. Weathering would break down the cement holding the grains together and the quartz would be transported away to form new quartz-rich sediments.

RS 13 would break down to form iron oxides from the biotite mica and clay minerals from the feldspar, and the rock would crumble to liberate grains of quartz and flakes of muscovite. If weathering and transport do not decompose feldspars and muscovite completely, a feldspar-rich sandstone (arkose) might be formed, and there might also be mica in some of the sandstone. However, the final end-product of prolonged transport would be silts or clays and quartz sands.

The minerals to be found in sediments from the weathering of RS 19 would be iron oxides, from the olivine and pyroxene, and clay minerals, from the plagioclase feldspar.

Question 7.6

The analysis resembles that of the claystone in Table 7.2 much more than those of the other two rocks. We would expect the rock to consist mainly of clay minerals.

Question 8.1

The most obvious source of heat is from igneous intrusions, but deep burial in the Earth's crust will also lead to an increase in temperature. Deep mines and drill holes provide evidence of the increase in temperature with depth.

Increased pressure may result from the weight of overlying rocks during deep burial. Pressure is also increased where two crustal plates are converging during mountain-building processes. This will be dealt with in greater detail in Block 3.

Question 8.2

The shiny, flat cleavage surfaces obvious with the hand lens are typical of biotite mica; in thin section this mineral has a brown colour and is strongly pleochroic in plane-polarized light.

Question 8.3

Phenocrysts are large, well-formed crystals in igneous rocks which have grown early in the cooling history of a magma, when there is little to hinder crystal growth. A rock containing phenocrysts is described as porphyritic, which unfortunately is confusingly similar to the term porphyroblastic.

Question 8.4

The garnet must have the highest surface energy because it forms the largest crystals.

Question 8.5

The rock is grey and very fine-grained, with closely spaced foliation planes. It is a slate.

Question 8.6

The two assemblages would be different. Even if both mudstones and basalt were to be subjected to the same temperature and pressure conditions during metamorphism, the chemical composition of basalt is very different from that of the mudstones. [*Comment*: in fact, at a moderate degree of metamorphism, the mudstones would be metamorphosed into schists not unlike RS 26, whereas the basalt would be metamorphosed into an amphibolite, such as RS 16.]

Question 8.7

RS 11 is a fine-grained metamorphic rock, a phyllite, and RS 26 is a coarse-grained and porphyroblastic (garnet-mica) schist. Both rocks are of similar composition, consisting mainly of quartz and muscovite. The larger grain size of RS 26 is the result of metamorphism under higher temperature and pressure conditions than in the case of RS 11.

Question 8.8

Both these rocks are porphyroblastic. Although it is difficult to see in the rock containing MS I, the matrix in both is probably dominated by quartz and muscovite mica. However, there are also compositional differences; the original sediment from which the rock containing MS I was formed must have contained a large amount of sulfide, which recrystallized to form the pyrite porphyroblasts on metamorphism, whereas the original material of RS 26 consisted almost entirely of silicate minerals, some of which recrystallized to form the garnet porphyroblasts. The grain size is also very different, and the rock containing MS I was formed at a lower pressure and temperature than RS 26.

Question 8.9

RS 17 is a crystalline rock without any mineral alignment, and this is the main textural criterion for identifying rocks as being of igneous origin. However, it is almost entirely made up of interlocking calcite crystals with a granulitic texture. The rock therefore must be a marble, formed by the metamorphic recrystallization of limestone.

ACKNOWLEDGEMENTS

Grateful acknowledgement is made to the following sources for permission to reproduce material in this Block:

Cover image copyright © Derek Hall; Frank Lane Picture Agency/Corbis; *Figure 2.21* Naomi Williams, Open University; *Figure 6.1* Dave Rothery, Open University; *Figure 7.4* Tucker, M. E. (1981) *Sedimentary Petrology: An Introduction*, Blackwell Scientific. Redrawn from Pettijohn, F. J. I. *et al.* (1973) *Sand and Sandstone*, Springer-Verlag; Fig*ure 7.6* J. A. Burnett, Micropalaenology Unit, Dept of Geological Sciences, University College, London; *Plates 6.1, 6.2, 6.8a, 6.11, 7.2bi* Dave Rothery, Open University; *Plate 6.3* Peter Sheldon, Open University; *Plates 6.4, 6.7, 6.9, 7.2a, 7.2bii, 8.1* Andy Tindle, Open University; *Plates 6.6, 6.10* Bryan Storey, British Antarctic Survey; *Plate 6.8b* Mark Davies, Open University; *Plates 7.1, 7.3* Angela Coe, Open University; *Plate 8.2* Chris Wilson, Open University; *Plate 9.1* Adapted by permission from Wicander, R. and Monroe, J. S. (1995) *Essentials of Geology*, copyright © 1995 Brooks/Cole Publishing Company, a division of International Thomson Publishing Inc. All rights reserved.

INDEX

Note: page numbers in **bold** are for terms that appear in the *Glossary* while page numbers in *italics* are for terms contained within Figures.